Blessed Robert Southwell

Blessed Robert Southwell

by D. H. MOSELEY

SHEED & WARD: NEW YORK

Acknowledgments

The quotations in this book are from late sixteenth century writings and records. Many of them became known to me through modern scholars to whom I am deeply grateful. I particularly thank Father Christopher Devlin, S.J. who, while engaged in research for his authoritative *The Life of Robert Southwell, Poet and Martyr* (Longmans, Green & Co. London, 1956), encouraged me to continue the account that I had undertaken, and generously forwarded newly discovered items that he thought might enliven it for young readers.

It would be impossible to name all the authors and editors to whom I am indebted for historical background, but each has my heartfelt gratitude.

D. H. M.

Blessed Robert Southwell

Chapter 1

At last, the darkness for which they had been waiting grew as dense as could be hoped for on a May night in Hampshire. The four young men who were huddled in a boat tied to a small dock in a creek near Warblington noticed that the sky was partially hidden by clouds; they wondered if the hour had finally arrived for their trusted boatmen Braye and Rogers to advise their tutor Master Smythe that they might put out for the brig anchored in the inlet. Since nightfall they had waited here, and now they were eager to begin their secret journey across the English Channel to Boulogne on the coast of France. The crossing had to be at night and secret because, in that year 1576, nobody was permitted to leave England to study at a foreign university without a license. To obtain a license, Braye's passengers, or their fathers, would have had to swear that Queen Elizabeth was the Supreme Governor of the Church in England. They were Catholics, loyal to the Pope, so they could not take this Oath of Supremacy.

"Braye is a cautious fellow," complained William Brooksby, pulling his heavy coat around his shoulders.

"Better cautious than caught," retorted Audley. "My

brother was recently reported by Sir Francis Walsingham's searchers when he was leaving Essex for France with a priest."

"Yes," agreed John Cotton, in a whisper. "We are all watched. Cousin Robert's brothers, Dick and Tom Southwell, were summoned this month before the Star Chamber because a spy claimed that they spoke lightly of Her Majesty."

"I heard that their father paid a fine of two hundred pounds for them," volunteered Brooksby. Then he turned to the young man who sat next to him, and continued, "I was amazed at their arrest, for your father conforms and goes to the Protestant services, doesn't he, Southwell?"

Robert Southwell, who had been listening to the others, answered reluctantly, "My father has been known to go to the Queen's Church. But my mother, who was Her Majesty's girlhood friend, is a staunch Catholic."

"Perhaps that is why your father did not obtain a license for you to study abroad," said Audley. "The rest of us had no choice. We Audleys are known to defy the law by having Mass celebrated in our house and sheltering priests; and Brooksby is connected with Lord Vaux of Harrowden, the boldest of Catholics, so he would be suspect. And you, Cotton—"

He was interrupted by low laughter.

"I am the son of George Cotton of Warblington, whose house in Fleet Street is always open to priests," said Cotton, giving Audley a poke in the ribs. "Small chance I would have to get a license!"

They were all silent a moment while they watched the low-scudding clouds. A light breeze was coming up, and the reeds in the marshes began to hum.

"I hate to leave England," confided Brooksby, "but I admit that I shall be glad to reach Douay, where we can hear Mass without the thought of being arrested. Perhaps I shall find

4

that I have a vocation to the priesthood. My confessor is not certain that I have."

"Mine expects me to be a priest," said Audley.

"I haven't a vocation," asserted John Cotton. "When I finish my studies, I shall return and help my father. But my cousin Robert considers—" He broke off.

They all strained their ears. An owl hooted in the distance; there was a splash as a small animal slid into the water. Then they heard the murmur of the tide and the slight creaking of their boat as it began to sway almost imperceptibly. Everybody except Southwell turned to look in the direction from which there came the thud of feet on the bank; they knew that the sound heralded the approach of Braye and Rogers, who were leading Master Smythe through the dark.

Robert Southwell did not turn. He was thinking. He had no doubt about his vocation. He felt certain of his call to the priesthood, certain that it was God's will that he dedicate his life to His service. But should he yield to his great yearning for contemplative prayer and spend his life as a Carthusian monk in a European monastery, or should he ask to be admitted to the Society of Jesus and, as a Jesuit, travel to the far-off Indies or Japan to convert the heathen? One other choice there might be, but he did not believe himself fitted for that: the work of a secular priest in England. His grandfather, Sir Richard Southwell, had been a bad man, and had helped King Henry VIII drive the monks and nuns from their monasteries; his own father conformed, and went to the Queen's services; his brothers were not renowned for virtue. He, a member of such a family, could not believe himself strong enough to return to England unless fortified by the vows of an order. No Jesuits had come to England and the Carthusians there had been killed.

"God will decide for me," he thought.

Just then Braye and Rogers loomed up out of the darkness, assisted Master Smythe to board the skiff, followed him, and cast off.

Robert Southwell, who had been in Douay for several months, was walking toward the chapel steps one bright autumn day wondering if the Flemish student John Deckers, whom he was to meet there, would recognize him. Then he remembered that Master Leonard Lessius, who taught both Deckers and himself at Anchin College of the University and who had arranged this meeting, would have told Deckers to speak to a slim, auburn-haired Englishman of medium height, who would approach from the direction of the English College where he lodged. At least, he would recognize Deckers, whom he had seen many times strolling with Master Leonard. Glad to be out of class, Southwell sauntered along the path, noticing how the sun shone through the linden trees that lined the quiet street, and gilded the leaves that were falling on the benches beneath them. As he was choosing a pleasant place to sit, he saw Deckers coming toward him without hesitation.

They smiled and shook hands, and Southwell, leading the way to a bench, asked, "Do you speak English?"

Deckers grinned amicably. "No," he replied in Latin, "but Master Leonard tells me that you speak Latin."

Southwell answered in Latin, "I have always had my lessons in Latin at home; all Englishmen do. But we pronounce it after our own fashion. Shall we sit on this bench and talk?"

Just as they were seating themselves, a hoop propelled by two barelegged urchins in black smocks bounded toward them. Each small boy held a long, narrow, hard-crusted loaf of bread with which he hit the hoop.

"Watch out for the hoop!" exclaimed Southwell in English. *"Cave trochum!"* he then shouted, remembering that he must speak Latin.

A burst of mirth escaped Deckers, and he explained, "I am not laughing at your pronunciation."

"You are happy at the thought that you do not have to eat those bread sticks," retorted Southwell, his eyes dancing. "We seem to be safe again," he continued as the boys sped on, their wooden shoes clattering on the pavement.

"Being from Hazebrouck, I laugh more than I talk," said Deckers. "We of the Low Countries are not great talkers, not garrulous like the French and Italians or. . . ." He paused for a word.

"Or communicative, like some of the English," supplied Southwell.

"Just so, communicative. Master Leonard said that you and I would be good friends and that he need not tell me anything about you, that you would attend to that."

Southwell laughed aloud. He picked up a fallen leaf and began to split it along its veins.

Deckers noticed his hands, the smooth hands of a gentleman, and he saw that his plain clothes and boots were of fine quality, a rich man's apparel.

Southwell gave Deckers a shy glance of appraisal, and then said, "It was my confessor who asked Master Leonard to arrange for you and me to meet."

"Perhaps he thought that you were lonely, so far from England and your family," suggested Deckers.

Southwell looked straight into Deckers' eyes. "No," he said, "he thought that I needed you to steady me."

"A heavy Flemish anchor!" Deckers chuckled.

"He was in earnest," continued Southwell. "I want to be a priest, but sometimes I have thought that I would be a Jesuit,

7

and again I have been sure that I preferred the life of a Carthusian. The other day, while we were discussing my vocation, we saw you walk by with Master Leonard. My confessor said that I should know you, that you had never wavered."

"Years ago," said Deckers, "I decided to be a Jesuit. But I may not be admitted to the Society of Jesus. The Superiors want only strong, brave men, not afraid to go on dangerous missions."

"The most dangerous place in the world for a priest is England," asserted Southwell.

"Then the Jesuits will go there. They love adventure," said Deckers. "I have heard that Queen Elizabeth claims to be the head of the Church there."

"There is some quibbling over words. She employs the term 'Supreme Governor of the Church.'"

"You are not considered loyal Englishmen if you are faithful to the Pope?" demanded John.

"We may be hanged or beheaded as traitors, even though we acknowledge Elizabeth as our true queen, if we do not swear that she rightfully rules the Church in England."

Deckers was silent for a moment, and then asked, "Is it true that it is against the law for Catholics to hear Mass in England?"

"Yes. The Government forbids the practice of our religion and fines us if we do not go to the Protestant services. Many Catholic noblemen are becoming poor. We Catholics who will not attend the Queen's church are called 'recusants,' an English word derived from *recusare,* of course."

"What is the English for *recusare*?" inquired Deckers.

"'To refuse,'" answered Southwell.

With a thick accent, Deckers repeated the words slowly, "'To refuse, to refuse, to refuse.'" Then he said, "Master Leonard told me that in order to get a degree at your universities of Oxford and Cambridge, a candidate must take the Oath of Supremacy."

"That is true. And that is why we recusants come to universities in France and Spain."

"I have seen many of you here in Douay, of course. I have always wondered about your rulers," said Deckers. Then he smiled winningly, and pleaded, "Explain to me how England came to be a Protestant country. You admit that you like to talk; here is a good opportunity."

"I did not say that I could give a lecture," said Robert, laughing. He threw away the leaf that he had been holding, picked up another, and began to separate the veins from the blade, leaving the tracery intact. "But I can understand why our recent history puzzles you. Shall I relate it very briefly? Put it, as we English say, 'in a nutshell'?"

The term amused Deckers. "Hark! A nutshell lecture!"

"And it is my first, remember. The audience is supposed to question.

"The trouble began when our Queen's father, King Henry VIII, asked the Pope to permit him to divorce his lawful wife, Queen Catherine of Aragon. The Pope refused. Henry then said that he was the head of the Church in England. He divorced Catherine, and had five wives after her."

"Wh-e-e-w!" exclaimed Deckers.

"He had two daughters: Mary, who was Queen Catherine's child, and Elizabeth, who was Anne Boleyn's. And he had one son, whose mother was Jane Seymour. When Henry died, the sickly young son became king and reigned as Edward VI. He was a Protestant, and claimed to be head of the Church like his father. When he died, Mary, who was a Catholic, became queen. She was loyal to the Pope. While she lived, many of the nobles who had become Protestants to please Henry or Edward became Catholics again. And when she died, Elizabeth, her half-sister, succeeded. She is a Protestant. Many of the nobles now think it wise to be Protestant."

"But if Elizabeth was illegitimate, how can she be the true queen?" demanded Deckers.

"Her father left her the right in his will. And our Parliament approved her succession when her brother and sister had died."

"But how can Catholics think her their queen? Wasn't she excommunicated by Pope Pius V in the Bull *Regnans in Excelsis*?"

"The Pope's Bull was never formally published in England. In all civil matters, we obey the sovereign approved by our Parliament," explained Robert.

"I heard some of the soldiers in the Low Countries say that Mary, Queen of Scots, is the rightful heir. Her grandfather was King Henry VII, and she is his legitimate descendant," said Deckers.

"Yes. Some claim that she should be Queen of England. She is a Catholic, and there are always rumors that Catholic gentlemen are plotting to put her on the throne. When her husband King Francis II of France died, she returned to Scotland, the very year that I was born. Six years later she had to abdicate the Scotch throne in favor of her small son. She took refuge in England. Ever since, she has been our Queen's prisoner in England."

"Because she is a Catholic?" asked Deckers.

"Not altogether that. It is hard to explain. Our Queen is not very religious. She is a Protestant but she would be a Catholic, or say that she was, if it suited her better. She wants to be the sovereign and rule England."

"It is all very complicated," said Deckers.

"And I do not think that I am supposed to discuss the matter. We Englishmen in Douay are advised to pray for our country but not to interest ourselves in its politics."

"Master Leonard told me that Dr. Allen, your Principal, founded the English College to be a home for English students at the University, and that he expects some of you to return to England as priests to minister to your countrymen," said Deckers.

"For that reason, he insists that we must be well grounded in theology."

"The Jesuits are fine theologians. You must become a Jesuit!" asserted Deckers.

"You suspect that it would be a great penance for me to be a silent Carthusian," said Southwell, smiling. "But I could pray and do penance, and perhaps serve England best if I were in a cloister, and—"

Deckers broke in, "It seems to me that your country needs the Jesuits. It would be wonderful if you would be a Jesuit and go home and convert the Queen!"

"Quite a proposition," said Southwell. "And I would have to convert her Secretaries, Sir William Cecil, who is Lord Burghley, and Sir Francis Walsingham. Walsingham is a convinced Protestant. He thinks that he must stamp out our religion. He is the head of the spy system, and has men called pursuivants or searchers watching Catholics in England and here on the Continent. They say that he can hear in London what is whispered in Rome, and that he has spies who are students in our Catholic colleges in Europe."

"Would there be a chance of your being a martyr if you went home an ordained priest?" asked Deckers.

"Best chance in the world—that is, if I remained a firm Catholic and refused to take the Oath of Supremacy."

"Then I know a future martyr," said Deckers.

Southwell studied his companion's face and, seeing its earnest expression, decided to tell about the weaknesses in his father's family and his reasons for fearing that he might not be brave. When he had explained that his father and brothers conformed, he described his grandfather's behavior, and added, "The house in which I was born was built on the site of an old Benedictine Priory, Horsham Saint Faiths, near Norwich in Norfolk. The place belonged to the monks, but my grandfather received it from King Henry VIII."

Deckers, who had listened carefully, asked, "How does it happen that you are a Catholic with a vocation for the priesthood?"

"I think that my mother and my tutor at home are responsible. My father had a priest living in our house to teach us. That is an old custom in England, you know. And my cousin Sir George Cotton of Warblington encouraged me and sent his son John and me over here to study. Would you like to come to dinner at the English College and meet Cotton and some of the English?"

Deckers grinned. "I hoped that you would ask me!"

Southwell rose from the bench. "I cannot offer you a fine dinner. The fare is very plain. But you will see a gathering of learned men at the High Table."

"Did they take the Oath of Supremacy to get their degrees?" asked Deckers, rising.

"Some of them did, before they knew how wrong it was. But later they were reconciled to the Church."

Then, without questioning each other, the two students removed their caps, went into the chapel and knelt before the Blessed Sacrament. Southwell prayed for England and for his mother and his sister Mary, who would soon be married to Edward Banister of Idsworth. The Banisters, like his mother's cousins the Cottons, Shelleys and Copleys, went to prison rather than deny their Faith. He prayed, too, for his sorely tempted father and brothers. Deckers knelt upright and prayed that Southwell might be a Jesuit and convert the Queen.

12

Rising, they paused a moment before Our Lady's shrine, and then went out into the warm air.

"We could not make such a visit in England," said Southwell. "We have no Catholic churches in which to reserve the Blessed Sacrament, for our churches were taken from us and our altars demolished. Even our private chapels are hidden rooms. And we have hiding places for the missals and altar vessels, and secret closets called 'priest's holes' where the clergy can take refuge when a house is searched."

"Life in England must be exciting," said Deckers.

"Very exciting," agreed Southwell, putting on his cap. "Let's go. It is almost dinner time. I'll race you to the 'Seminary'—we often call our college that."

Off they went, their scholars' gowns flying out behind them.

Two stolid merchants extended their arms to protect wares displayed on the pavement. "Students will be students," said one.

"English students will be English students," said the other. "I hate the English!"

Chapter 2

When Southwell and Deckers were ready for dinner, they found that they had a moment to wait in the corridor before going into the dining hall.

"Would you like to see our Douay Diary?" asked Southwell. "It is a register in which the comings and goings of students and visitors are recorded. It is written in Latin. Sometimes we Englishmen scarcely recognize our own names when they are made into Latin. There are many visitors, for Dr. Allen wants all Englishmen to feel at home here. Even merchants and travelers can stay thirty days free if they are poor. And often the students' fathers are our guests when they bring their sons from England."

They went into the office, paused before the book, and read the recent entries.

"Why, here your arrival is noted!" exclaimed Deckers, and he pointed to the lines: *1576: June 10 Mr. Cotton and Mr. Southwell, noblemen's sons both, were brought to us by the same messenger from England.* Then he read further. "And this entry tells of your coming over to Anchin to have your lessons with the Jesuits: *This month the noblemen Mr. Pudseus and Mr. Southwell were received from us at Anchin College.*" Deckers regarded Southwell thoughtfully and said, "That will be a valuable record of your life when you are a Jesuit martyr."

Southwell smiled and said, "So you are making me both Jesuit and martyr at this early date. But come, the dons are filing into the dining hall and I want to point them out to you. There is a rumor that some of them will soon be leaving for Rome to found an English College there. Dr. Allen consulted the Pope about it last fall."

Standing in the shadow and speaking softly, Southwell indicated Dr. Allen, Principal of the English College, whose idea it had been to found this home and seminary for students and English candidates for the priesthood. "There is Allen, with the short beard and pleasant face. He was once Principal of Saint Mary's Hall at Oxford."

"I recognize him," whispered Deckers. "He holds a Chair of Divinity in the University of Douay."

"And the man behind him who looks so English is Dr. Richard Bristowe. You must have seen him often, for his

14

mother and sister are refugees in Douay. They will be here in the dining hall after dinner, for they come with the other English residents on half-holidays for the discourses." Southwell paused a moment, then he nudged Deckers gently and remarked, "The next in line is Dr. Gregory Martin. He is directing the translation of the Bible into English for the uneducated, who cannot read it in Latin as we do. I have known about him always, for he was tutor in the Duke of Norfolk's household and taught Philip Howard, the Duke's son. My grandfather and Philip's were friends."

By this time the students were following the dons into the dining hall. Southwell and Deckers joined them, and after grace seated themselves at one of the three long tables. Straightway, a reader at a raised lectern began to read passages from the Old Testament in Latin. Many of the students, who had risen in time for morning devotions before five o'clock Mass, were sleepy; they gave attention, nevertheless.

John Deckers noticed that some of the guests were not much interested in the reading, and discovered to his dismay that his own mind was on the quality of the soup. "Cabbage soup, turnip soup or what is it?" he kept asking himself. He remembered that his plump Flemish mother, who put cream into almost every dish, said that the English cooked with water, but he did not know that less than a year before, Dr. Gregory Martin had written his Jesuit friend Edmund Campion about the Seminary soup. . . . "nearly sixty men and youths of the greatest promise were seated at three tables contentedly eating a little broth, thickened with nothing save the commonest roots; you could have sworn that they were feasting on such English delicacies as stewed raisins and plums."

Presently some of the English refugees filed in. The Bible reader closed the Old Testament, and the English discourses began. Southwell listened attentively while Deckers examined the assembly. When the discourses were finished, the new-

15

comers were greeted by courteous Dr. Allen, and the guests began to mingle.

John Cotton and other students joined Southwell and Deckers. There was talk of England, and references to the Tower of London and its many separate towers and dungeons where Englishmen were imprisoned for their Faith. Then the talk shifted to the Wars of Religion in the Low Countries and the resentment to the English developing among the townspeople of Douay. The students, drawn to a group of their elders, heard Dr. Bristowe say, "Already there is a feeling that we shall have to send our students elsewhere."

"Where?" asked the guest whom he addressed.

"The young ones will go with their tutors to Paris, to the Jesuit College of Clermont, at the University. The University of Paris is trying to oust the Jesuits, but the Pope agrees to their having a college there. Dr. Thomas Darbyshire, who was once Dean of Saint Paul's and Chancellor of London, is in Paris; he will be equal to keeping an eye on our young students."

"And the others, the older ones?"

"That is not decided. If the Calvinists continue to incite the townspeople of Douay against the English residents, we shall move some of the older students. Dr. Gregory Martin already plans to take a number with him when he goes to Rome to begin work at the new English College. That College is to be opened where the 14th Century English Hospital for Pilgrims has been, in the Via di Monserrato."

"Oh, I know the spot near the Campo dei Fiori, across from where Father Philip Neri lives, and just a few steps from where Ignatius Loyola's church was."

"Yes, and. . . ." Dr. Bristowe and his companion moved off, but John Deckers and Robert Southwell had heard enough to throw them into a state of excitement.

16

"Clermont College in Paris is a Jesuit house like Anchin in Douay," said Deckers.

"Yes. But think of an English College in Rome! And Father Philip Neri across the square! They call him the Apostle of Rome. It is said that he loves the Blessed Sacrament the way Saint Thomas Aquinas did." Then Southwell added, somewhat timidly, as he walked to the door with Deckers, "I have translated some of Saint Thomas Aquinas' verses from Latin into English. I confessed to you that I like to talk, and you may as well know the worst: I also like to write."

Deckers stood in the doorway and looked out a moment, then he turned to Southwell and said very earnestly, "The Jesuits are expected to write. They are even required to write what are called 'Relations,' accounts of their missionary work, for their Superiors. Good-bye, and thank you. We shall both be Jesuits, Southwell."

Having seen Deckers walk off with the other guests, Southwell went to his desk, picked up some pages crisscrossed with writing, and began to read to himself his English rendition of the Sequence that Saint Thomas Aquinas wrote for the Mass of Corpus Christi. He had given it its Latin title *Lauda Sion Salvatorem,* but he took a pen and wrote instead, *"Of the Blessed Sacrament of the Altar."* Then he considered very carefully the lines that he had found most difficult to translate into English, those in which Saint Thomas had made it clear that Our Lord is in each part of the consecrated Host:

> When the priest the Host divideth
> Know that in each part abideth
> All that the whole Host covered.
>
> Form of bread, not Christ is broken
> Not of Christ, but of His token
> Is state or stature altered.

17

"I love the poem because I love the Holy Eucharist," he thought, "and when I am a priest, I shall do as Dr. Allen does and urge young people to go to Holy Communion frequently. I wish I could improve my translation of this verse:

> Angels' bread made pilgrims' feeding,
> Truly bread for children's eating."

John Cotton came into the room. "So you are to be a Jesuit?"

Southwell waved the page he held. "Jesuit Superiors will decide."

Chapter 3

Some weeks after the meeting with Deckers, a rap on his door startled Southwell. He pushed under a huge volume the paper on which he had been writing English verse, ran his fingers through his auburn hair, and rose to open the door.

"Come in."

The old porter, much flustered, entered from the corridor. "It's his lordship," he announced, "your uncle, Sir Thomas Copley, Lord Copley of Gatton, Baron of Welles and . . . well, his lordship's retinue from Antwerp or Louvain or wherever he may be residing at the moment. Dr. Allen and all the Doctors and Masters are in the hall listening to him, and—"

"Yes. Every one does listen," interrupted Southwell. "And he asked for me?"

"Dr. Allen sent me for you, sir. And if you are not too

busy with your studies, you are to descend without delay. He is a grand lord, and what the cook can provide, I cannot imagine."

"He is not such an important person as is sometimes supposed," said Southwell consolingly, and then his tender conscience hurt, for he had been thinking that here was Uncle Thomas tired of strutting like a peacock in Belgium, and about to get himself knighted by King Henry III of France.

"I shall be down immediately," he assured the messenger, who left, closing the door behind him. Southwell dropped to his knees and remained a second, his thin hands clasped. He prayed for patience with his Uncle Thomas, his mother's brother who, having been a Protestant when Catholic Queen Mary ruled, was now a Catholic to the displeasure of his Protestant sovereign Queen Elizabeth. Sir Thomas Copley's genius for display irked his nephew.

Southwell rose from his knees, made himself presentable, and sped down the corridors and stairway to the hall where the company was gathered listening, of course, to Sir Thomas.

"Here he is. He is a good student," volunteered Dr. Allen as Southwell entered and greeted the assembly.

"Not given to writing verse occasionally?" taunted Sir Thomas; and then added, "ah, well, writing is a family weakness with us Copleys and Shelleys. With the English in general, perhaps. You remember that his late Majesty King Henry VIII wrote very well in his day. My son Henry is his namesake. And Her Majesty is gifted in a literary way. She is Henry's godmother. As for me, Lord Burghley would tell you that I exercise my bent by writing to him explaining that, although I choose to live on the Continent because I am a Catholic (converted by disagreeing with Jewel, the Protestant divine), I am determined to keep my English estates intact for my family."

Southwell cast a glance at gentle Dr. Allen, whose serene

face betrayed nothing but interest in his guest, and then he tried to listen patiently himself.

"How is Lady Katherine?" someone asked.

"Well. Charming. A most beautiful mother for my children, Henry named for the King, William, Margaret, Anthony and . . . and others, of course. My wife goes back and forth to England, always interested in keeping in touch with our large connection. This lad's mother, by the way. . . ."

Dr. Allen rose and said courteously that Sir Thomas doubtless had family matters to discuss with his nephew. As the other gentlemen withdrew with him, Southwell found himself alone with his uncle.

"Did Aunt Katherine bring news of my mother?" he questioned. "How is she?"

"Ah, as always . . . quiet, unruffled, but determined. Your father and Dick and Tom are, like the other Southwells, worldly. It is fortunate that your mother is a good Catholic. Your aunt says that your sister Mary grows more and more like our side of the family: very pretty, of course . . . hair somewhat like yours, but it curls. And blue eyes . . . deep blue. Small wonder young Edward Banister of Idsworth fell in love with her! When she marries, she will be a neighbor of the Cottons of Warblington, you know. Sir George Cotton, by the way, suffers almost as much for his religion as I do. That is, although he has not had to leave the country to preserve his estates, he is a recusant and pays fines that will impoverish him.

"But to return to our own affairs. Your father still conforms, goes to the Queen's Protestant services and is in favor at Court. He drew up a document for me that will protect my house in London and Gatton, the Surrey place on which I spent such large sums before I came abroad for conscience's sake. Ah! What I suffer for my religion! Still, we are not without resources. The French King will knight me, and I am not unknown to the European churchmen. My uncle, your grand-uncle, Sir Richard Shelley, Grand Prior of England, is in Rome. The Italians call him *Signor Conchilia* . . . 'shell' . . . *conchilia*. Quite poetical. And, by the way, I brought a copy of my new will to read to you. I write wills and codicils to wills just as I write letters to Lord Burghley. We Copleys must have a literary outlet. Whatever you do, don't write."

Sir Thomas paused, and began to open a document that lay on the table in front of him. Southwell repressed a sigh and tried to seem interested while his uncle scanned the lines until he came to the passage he sought, and exclaimed, "Ah, here it is. I want you to know that I am leaving certain keepsakes to your mother because she, as a Catholic, will value them: 'I give unto my most entirely beloved sister Mrs. Southwell over and besides the ring (before bequeathed to her) that ring that Cardinal Hosius sent me with the elk hoof enclosed in it . . .' "

"I feel sure that your thoughtfulness will please my mother."

"Yes. And the ring will do for you when you are a Cardinal."

"But I plan to be a Jesuit, a plain missionary priest, if the Society will admit me, so I shall never be a Cardinal," protested Southwell.

"Maybe. Maybe," muttered Sir Thomas, rolling up his will. "But, on both sides of your family, there is a gift for high places . . . not Tower Hill or the gibbet at Tyburn. We leave Tower Hill to the Howards. I would hate to try to count the Southwells at Court, no matter what religion is in fashion."

Southwell's face flushed and his uncle, noticing it, said, "Well, well. I wonder if you could send word that I am staying the night here at the Seminary. The soup is said to be thin, but I am on my way to the French King and this is a good place to rest the horses."

Chapter 4

Robert Southwell and John Deckers crammed the autumn days full. Every minute not occupied with other duties they spent together studying, making their visits to the Blessed Sacrament, and, of course, discussing the means by which they would become Jesuits. All their pursuits were not serious, and they took walks through the city of Douay, then an important commercial town. Had Southwell not had a marvelous gift for seeming almost a part of the landscape, for being wherever he pleased without being much in evidence, their expeditions might have ended disastrously, for the English were increasingly unpopular. As it was, they went their way in peace, and began a lifelong friendship.

Dr. Allen and Dr. Bristowe decided that existence in Douay was dangerous for the English. Dr. Gregory Martin set out for Rome, taking with him some of the older students who were to live at the new English College. That same month, November 1576, some priests and theological students and a number of young English noblemen departed for Paris. Among these were Robert Southwell, the Cotton brothers, William Brooksby, the Audleys and various others belonging to prominent recusant families. With them was their tutor, Mr. Thomas Smythe. Deckers stayed behind at Anchin College in Douay.

The English students went to the Collège de Clermont, a Jesuit institution in the rue Saint Jacques, founded in 1564 against the protest of the Faculty of the University of Paris. Its Jesuit professors were chiefly Italian and Spanish.

The young Englishmen, watched over by their tutor, lodged near the college. So far from home, they became close friends. But even then there were matters that Southwell did not want to discuss with anyone, and he formed the habit of writing out his thoughts. When his heart was very full, he prayed pen in hand.

At Douay, he had heard Dr. Bristowe mention an English priest who had been Dean of Saint Paul's and Chancellor of London in the days of Catholic Queen Mary, who was now living in Paris. Southwell now learned that this Dr. Thomas Darbyshire was to be his confessor and director. He was surprised that a man so learned and important had time for his young fellow countrymen, but he was to discover that Dr. Darbyshire was never happier than when with young people.

Southwell had been in Paris only a few days when, pausing for a visit to a neighboring church, he saw a pleasant English priest teaching a group of children catechism. The class was about to be dismissed, and as Southwell left the church the priest joined him.

"You are one of our English students?" he asked, as they walked along together.

"Yes, sir. Robert Southwell, newly arrived from Douay."

"Ah, I remember your grandfather, Sir Richard Southwell. Queen Mary chose him to escort the Princess Elizabeth. He was a Catholic at that time, of course."

Southwell looked up quickly. "You must be Mr. Dr. Darbyshire. But you were teaching children catechism and. . . ."

"Oh, I like to teach the little ones. I learn much from the young," he replied, smiling kindly at Southwell.

"Master Smythe, my tutor, told me that you would be my confessor. You cannot imagine how thankful I am to discover that you already know about my family . . . my grandfather, and perhaps my father, too."

"Yes, about both of them. It is true that your grandfather did many things for which he was doubtless sorry. But God is merciful."

Southwell thought that God was indeed merciful to send him a confessor who knew how weak members of his family could be, how his grandfather had helped King Henry VIII drive the monks and nuns out of their convents, and then enriched himself with their property; how he had betrayed his boyhood friend, the Earl of Surrey, the poet; how he had changed from Catholic to Protestant or Protestant to Catholic whenever there was a change in the sovereign's religion. And who knew that his own father protected himself by going to the Queen's Protestant services.

Presently, when they had walked on a few paces, he looked up and said, "But my father is a Catholic at heart. We had a priest to tutor us at home. He and my mother taught me. But . . . well, I may as well tell you right away that I am always afraid that a person with a family like mine ought not to—" He stopped suddenly.

"Ought not to expect to be strong enough in the Faith to be a priest," Father Darbyshire finished for him. "You could not be strong enough without God's help. None of us could, especially in these days when priests in England are racked and hanged for their religion. So you want to be a priest?"

"Yes, Father. A priest and a Jesuit. When I was a boy staying with my cousins, the Cottons in Sussex, I learned about the Jesuits, and I thought that I would like to go to the Indies or Japan. Then later I thought that I wanted to be a Carthusian monk and give all my life to prayer."

"Prayer is a primary service. I, too, thought of being a Carthusian," said Dr. Darbyshire.

24

"But you are a Jesuit!" exclaimed Southwell.

"Yes. There is room for many kinds of men in the Society of Jesus," explained the priest.

"Even for men who like to write. That is one of my faults, Father. I write verse and sometimes I write not Latin verse but English. And, occasionally, I even write English prose."

"Well, you will be an articulate penitent; one after my own heart. By the way, if you are Richard Southwell's son, you are Sir Thomas Copley's nephew."

Southwell was startled. "Oh, I hoped he would not know that I was in Paris. The French King is going to. . . ." He broke off.

". . . Knight him and his son Henry to compensate for their living in exile abroad," finished Father Darbyshire. "That is not a secret."

"Uncle Thomas does not have secrets," said Southwell. "I suppose you know that. . . ."

"Oh, yes! I know the worst. He is going to make a Cardinal of you. You are to have Cardinal Hosius' ring." Father Darbyshire laughed.

Southwell laughed, too. "It is certainly not my vocation to be a Cardinal. Could I best avoid the Red Hat as a Jesuit or a Carthusian?"

"As I understand it, the Society is not eager to admit you, because of your youth perhaps. . . ."

"Oh, Father, do you think that I will be a Jesuit?"

"Time will tell. Here we are at the College, and I am glad, for I have a game leg and these streets are rough. But you are young and if I were you, I would explore Paris a bit. The University is objecting to students' having horses but is not restricting the use of their feet. Go to Saint Séverin and Notre Dame and to Montmartre where Ignatius Loyola, Francis Borgia and the other first Jesuits took their vows. You need

25

not go to Court. Your Uncle Thomas might catch you and try to make you take dancing and fencing lessons."

They parted with an engagement for their first interview and Southwell, lighter hearted than he had been since his arrival in Paris, rushed to his lodgings and routed out Cotton, Brooksby and the Audleys, who were hugging a smoky fire.

"Come on out. Mr. Dr. Darbyshire said that we were to go to Saint Séverin and Notre Dame and Montmartre and—"

"Hurray," shouted Brooksby, seizing his cap and throwing John Cotton his. "That is the kind of confessor to have." He hesitated a moment. "He isn't going with us, is he?"

"No. He has a game leg. But you would not object to having him along, even though he was once Dean of Saint Paul's."

Out they went into the December sunshine. They tramped down the Rue Saint Jacques toward the River Seine. Southwell and Cotton were in the lead, and presently darted into a narrow, crooked street. Followed at a rapid pace by the others, they reached a weathered Gothic church, and paused a moment at the entrance. Removing their caps, all entered together, made the Sign of the Cross with holy water as they passed the stoup, and dropped on their knees before the tabernacle. Then Southwell pointed to a stained glass window and said softly, "That must be the Thomas à Becket window, Saint Thomas of Canterbury."

They stood in a group and studied the many-colored glass, each remembering some event in the martyr's story that had been familiar to them all their lives.

"He was a student here in Paris, you know," said Brooksby.

"Yes, and when he returned to England, he expected an easy life," added Cotton.

"I don't think the King knew he would stand up to him so defiantly when he was made an Archbishop," one of the Audley brothers said.

"But once he was an Archbishop, he had to defend the rights of the Church," put in Southwell.

"Yes, 'Father Robert.' And he got martyred for his pains, just as you will," taunted Brooksby, laughing.

"And you," retorted Robert.

"Master Smythe says that if I don't get rid of this Paris cough, I'll not live to mount the scaffold," said Brooksby. "Come, let's get out of doors."

"I suggest we run all the way to Notre Dame and climb the North Tower for exercise," said Cotton, when they were outside.

Away they sped, five ruddy-faced young Englishmen, brushing by French pedestrians and causing black-garbed crones to mutter, "How handsome and young they are, these English! And how carefree!"

And truly, they seemed not to have a care in the world when, having crossed the bridge to the island in the Seine on which the vast Cathedral of Notre Dame stood, they hurried to the entrance to the building's North Tower and accosted a white-haired man who sat at the foot of the circular stair mending a rush-seated chair.

"Too late, too late," muttered the tower guardian. "I am busy. I cannot mount with you today. Tomorrow. Come back tomorrow."

Brooksby jingled several coins. Southwell commented on the old man's work. Cotton found two or three pennies and rattled them in his pocket, while he said in French, "Let's spend our money on ale."

The old man rose, took a huge iron key from where it lay on the stone ledge beside him and grumbled, "I cannot mount the stairs, but. . . ."

Straightway, all the coins were his, and he cautioned, "Fast.

27

Hurry. Do not linger. Night falls early in December." He turned the great key in the gate and admitted them to the stairway. They rushed up the first steps.

"Night certainly falls early in the North Tower," said Cotton, who was in the lead. "It is pitch black on these stairs. But come on!"

Up and up they climbed, their hands feeling for the cold stone walls, the toes of their boots striking the angled stone stairs. Brooksby, who had let the others precede him, paused and coughed now and then. Presently Southwell and he slackened their pace, while the rest clambered ahead.

"I counted three hundred and seventy-five steps," shouted Cotton, pausing in the doorway to the roof. Southwell and Brooksby joined the others and stood close to the ugly gargoyles carved on the ends of the gutters. They looked down on Paris spread beneath them. The buildings of the city were gray, and the silver Seine wound its way toward the sea. The sunlight was pale and a wan sky arched the whole scene.

"The hill over there is Montmartre," said Southwell. "It was in the chapel of Saint Denis there that Ignatius Loyola, Francis Xavier and their companions made their first vows as Jesuits."

"Yes, 'Father Robert,' " his friends replied. "Jesuits. Always you talk about Jesuits. Why not tell about Saint Denis walking there carrying his head in his hands?"

"Because that is a legend, and Jesuits are real," Southwell reminded them.

"The wind is cold here," said Brooksby, shivering.

"Yes. And the steps might get even darker if we linger," said Cotton.

The five scrambled down, recklessly defying the darkness. Shouting their thanks, they burst past the old guardian, who had put his work aside for the day.

"Come. We may not get here again soon," said Southwell. "Let's look at the sculpture on the portal."

Sombered, they stood and marveled at the beauty of the ancient carving that represented the Enthronement of Our Lady.

Presently the others moved on, but Southwell lingered. He was experimenting with words for a verse for the Blessed Virgin:

Gem to her worth, spouse to her love ascends.
Prince to her throne, Queen to her heavenly King
Whose court with solemn pomp on her attends,
And choirs of saints with greeting notes do sing.
Earth rendereth up her undeserved prey.
Heaven claims the right, and bears the prize away.

"Oh, what is the use?" he asked himself. "I could never describe Mary in Heaven."

All that winter and the following spring, Southwell studied in Paris. On June 15, 1577, he returned to Douay with his tutor. His arrival was noted in the College Diary. Within a few weeks, three Marshall boys arrived from England with their father, and John Gerard, a fearless English student, also came. Southwell was determined to be a Jesuit, and he and John Deckers requested admission to the Society of Jesus. Deckers was told that he could go to the novitiate at Tournai, and was admitted there in May 1578. Southwell was refused by the Superiors. About a week after Deckers was admitted, the Tournai novitiate was closed because of the Wars of Religion, and the novices were dismissed.

Southwell suggested to Deckers that they go to Rome and seek admission there, but Deckers decided not to make the journey across the Alps; a nine-hundred-mile walk did not appeal to him. However, one of the Marshall boys, Matthew, volunteered to go. Since Nicholas Smith, a nephew of South-well's Aunt Katherine Copley, was about to set out from Paris for Rome, Southwell and Marshall went to Paris and made the journey with him.

Chapter 5

Three weary, travel-stained young men knocked at the door of the English College close to the River Tiber. Before their knock was answered, they were startled by a great clanging of bells, and realized that it was the hour of the Ave Maria, and that the bells of all of the hundreds of Roman churches were ringing the Angelus.

They lifted their caps and recited the prayer, "The Angel of the Lord declared unto Mary. . . ."

When they had finished, the porter arrived. They gave their names, Robert Southwell, Matthew Marshall and Nicholas Smith. The porter admitted them and disappeared, leaving them standing in a semi-dark entry from which they could see a small garden. They had waited only an instant when a fine looking Englishman, much their senior, came to them at the porter's summons.

"Welcome," he said. "I am Sherwin. You will be in my dormitory. Doubtless you want to wash and stow away your belongings before you meet anyone. Come."

They followed him to a room in which there were six beds.

He assigned a bed to each, showed them their desks, the presses in which their clothes would be, and left them for a few moments while they washed and put on fresh clothes.

"My! What a relief to get out of these boots," exclaimed Marshall.

"Mine are worn so thin I could feel the pebbles on the road," said Smith.

Southwell made no remark. He was contentedly examining his surroundings, feeling thankful that Ralph Sherwin would be head of his dormitory, and determining to ask the calm Englishman to help him apply for admission to the Society of Jesus. He was sure that whatever Sherwin did would be well done.

When they were ready, Sherwin came to the door and said, "Let's go down to the hall. You will wish to greet our Warden, Dr. Clenock, and your friend Dr. Gregory Martin and some of the students."

He led them swiftly down the stone stair where the porter was already lighting small hanging lamps. Then, motioning, he opened a door and shepherded them into a chapel, or small church.

Southwell's heart leaped with joy as they knelt before the tabernacle. "My Lord and my God!" he thought and then silently said the prayer, dear to Ignatius Loyola, called the *Suscipe*:

"Receive, O Lord, all my liberty. Take my memory, my understanding, and my entire will. Whatsoever I have or hold, Thou hast given it; I give it all back to Thee and commit it wholly to be governed by Thy will. Thy love and Thy grace give unto me, and I am rich enough and ask for nothing more."

Then he added the prayer that he might be a Jesuit, return to England to be a missioner among Catholics and a martyr for the Faith.

Sherwin rose, led them out of the chapel, and preceded them to a room from which came the sound of conversation. Southwell, entering, saw gentle Dr. Gregory Martin, the translator of the Scriptures, standing in the midst of a group. Sherwin led the new arrivals to the Warden and presented them. Then Southwell went to greet Dr. Martin, who received him with delight and introduced him cheerfully to the Jesuit Father Robert Persons, who was spending the evening at the College.

"Father, Southwell has walked nine hundred miles to meet you. He has a keen desire to be a member of the Society of Jesus, an English Jesuit like yourself and Father Edmund Campion."

Southwell gave Dr. Martin a grateful smile for smoothing his way, and then let himself be led by Father Persons to a group of students who had joined Sherwin, Marshall and Smith. Their names had a pleasant English sound, Luke Kirby, John Shert, Richard Haddock, George Haydock, Martin Aray and others. And, although they were older than he, Southwell felt at ease with them.

A bell rang and the company filed into the refectory. Southwell thought of Douay, and of how he had watched Dr. Martin there with Dr. Allen and the other professors, and he realized that arrangements at the Roman English College much resembled those there: the grace, the tables, the reading aloud during the meal. But he was surprised to see the white linen and table napkins, the gleaming glass, the place settings that included forks for every student; forks were seldom or never seen in England. And the fare was more delicate than he had expected. He was hungry, and the cold meat and salad, bread and cheese and grapes were welcome.

After supper, when grace had been said, they went back to the hall. There they sat, and Southwell, on a bench close to his elders, listened eagerly to the conversation, especially when it

turned to England and the Catholics there. He had been for
months with foreigners at Anchin College, and many weeks on
the way to Rome, and it warmed his heart to hear Englishmen discussing England in his native tongue. The wars in the
Low Countries were discussed, also, and conditions in Spain
and France. And, of course, there were conjectures as to
Queen Elizabeth's marriage: would she marry the Duke of
Anjou in order to ally England with France? If she did so,
the conditions of Catholics in the realm might improve, for the
French royal family was Catholic.

The recusants in England were still suffering for their religion, and Southwell, anxious for news of his family, listened
carefully to Dr. Martin, whose home had been near that of his
Sussex kin. But there was no mention of any of them.

Someone said to Dr. Martin, "We understand that you and
Cuthbert Mayne, who was martyred last fall, were friends
when you were at Oxford."

"Yes, he and Edmund Campion were at Saint John's College when I was. Later, we were all reconciled to the Church
and studied at Douay. Campion entered the Society of Jesus.
Mayne was ordained priest, returned to England and labored
among the Catholics."

Sherwin turned to Southwell, saying, "Perhaps you have
not heard the details of Cuthbert Mayne's last days. He was
arrested and accused of having said Mass and of having a copy
of the Papal Bull about the Jubilee of 1575 in his possession."

John Shert added, "He stood up to the crowd. They offered
him his life if he would renounce his religion, and they urged
him to swear on the Bible that the Queen was the Supreme
Governor of the Church in England. If he refused, he was to
be hanged, drawn and quartered. He took the Bible in his
hands, made the Sign of the Cross upon it, kissed it, and said,

'The Queen never was, nor is, nor ever shall be the head of the Church in England.' "

"Of course, he paid the penalty," added Dr. Martin, "and is the first, or proto-martyr of our Douay Seminary."

"The Seminary priests have given new courage to the re-cusants," said Luke Kirby.

"That is true," answered Dr. Martin, "but Dr. Allen feels that they need the Jesuits to help them. What do you think about that, Father Persons? Do you think that your Father General will ever send Jesuits to England?"

Southwell listened with all his might for Father Persons' reply. The latter, rising, said, "I do not know. If he decides to do so, I think that English Jesuits will hope to be chosen for the mission. I must say good night now, Dr. Clenock, for I have matters to attend to for our novitiate before bedtime. I have enjoyed the evening with my fellow countrymen."

Sherwin walked to the door with the Jesuit, and then re-turned to the recently arrived Englishmen. "Let's go to the chapel for our night prayers, and then get to bed. You must be very tired."

An hour later Southwell, about to fall asleep, thought of the evening's talk, and his mind harked back to his first meet-ing with John Deckers and his belief that Jesuits would eventu-ally go to England.

During Southwell's first few days in Rome, he looked to Sherwin for everything. Sherwin was not a Jesuit, but he longed for the new English College to be in charge of the Society of Jesus. He and some of the other serious English students thought that the Rector did not understand that they wished thorough preparation for their mission and a disciplined life that would fit them for it.

What had brought Southwell to Rome was his keen desire to enter the Jesuit Novitiate, and so his first act was to apply for admission. While he waited for an answer, Sherwin showed him the city.

They crossed the Tiber and walked around the vast new Church of Saint Peter. The dome that Michelangelo had designed was not finished, but altars were being placed, and the marble was bright and shiny in the clear Italian light. Then they went up the Janiculum Hill. Sherwin pointed out the Alban Hills in the distance. They looked down on the city, the winding yellow river, the crooked streets and vine-covered ruins that Southwell would come to know so well.

In the city itself, huge new churches were rising, for there was a great revival of religion. Sherwin pointed out one church that he called the *Chiesa Nuova,* or New Church, and not far away the site of the new Roman College that Pope Gregory XIII, who was reigning, had ordered built.

One bright afternoon they visited the Roman Forum and the Colosseum, the Palatine Hill, and the ruins of the Golden House of Nero. All of these walks delighted Southwell and his companions, and helped pass the time while they waited for news from the Superior of the Jesuits.

Southwell was alone in the garden when Sherwin approached and said, "Come. I have a few moments, and I want to show you our own neighborhood and have you meet one of our near neighbors."

As they passed the porter's desk, Sherwin took two pegs from a long box and stuck them into holes in a board. "Your peg and mine," he explained. "Each of us has a hole, and whenever we go out we put a peg in it, so that it will be known that we are not at home."

They stepped out into the street and started across the square on which the small Church of San Girolamo della Carità faced. A white-haired priest, standing beside the church, called out, *"Salvete flores martyrum,"* and waved gaily.

35

"He addresses us in Latin, not in Italian!" exclaimed Southwell, "and with the line from Prudentius' Hymn for the Feast of Holy Innocents, 'Hail Flowers of Martyrdom.' Why that greeting?"

"Because we are young and English and destined for martyrdom. That is Father Philip Neri. He is called the Apostle of Rome. Come. I thought that he might be here, and I brought you out to meet him."

Sherwin led Southwell over to the tall thin priest, who wore a threadbare cassock.

"This is Robert Southwell, Father Philip. He is living with us because the Jesuits will not receive him. They do not like his auburn hair, perhaps, or maybe they refuse him because he writes verse." Sherwin was laughing.

"Writing verse is not always a sin," said Father Philip, putting his slender hand on Southwell's shoulder. "And the Jesuits will receive him later, of course. They are cautious in such matters." His eyes twinkled. "Ignatius Loyola was my good friend." His hand was still on Southwell's shoulder as he guided them into the ancient church, saying, "This is where Saint Paula and her daughter Eustochium lived. They were friends of Saint Jerome, who translated the Scriptures into Latin."

Father Philip knelt before the tabernacle. Kneeling beside him, Southwell felt that he saw the expression of perfect devotion to the Blessed Sacrament. Getting to his feet, the old priest pointed to a plain confessional. "That is where you will find me always until I celebrate Mass at noon. Sometimes the young men who are early risers come to my room and wake me to hear their confessions."

They were approaching an open door, and Father Philip indicated the way across a courtyard to an upstairs room. "That is the Oratorio," he explained. "The young men who walk with me to the Catacombs and the Seven Churches come back here and we have night prayers in the Oratorio. You know Italian? You like verse? You will learn our hymns. We Italians love to sing, and we sing of Our Lady and the Angels."

Southwell realized suddenly that Father Philip had spoken throughout in Italian, and that he, who had had a few Italian lessons at home, had understood every word. He determined to put in some of his spare time perfecting himself in the language.

"But I am delaying your walk," said Father Philip. "Hurry, get on with your expedition."

"Yes, Father," said Sherwin, dropping to his knees and pulling Southwell down with him. "But bless us first, please."

When they returned to the English College, Southwell received word that he would be enrolled for the Jesuit novitiate.

Chapter 6

October 17, 1578, the Eve of the Feast of Saint Luke, Robert Southwell was enrolled among the young men who would study to be Jesuits. He left the English College, which was down near the Tiber, and moved up to the Jesuit Novitiate of Sant' Andrea on the Quirinal Hill. Matthew Marshall and Nicholas Smith went with him. Father Robert Persons, the English Jesuit whom they had met, was in charge of the English novices in Rome, and he had already prepared them for the change from the College to the Novitiate.

At Sant' Andrea, they were greeted by an Englishman who had been at Douay and who had insisted on making the journey to Rome just as Southwell had. This was Simon Hunt. He was older than they, and had been a Protestant, taking his degree at Oxford.

Hunt received the newcomers cordially, and showed them their quarters. Southwell, noting the movement everywhere, men sweeping the halls, dusting furniture, scrubbing stairs and weeding the garden, thought that he had not seen so many servants in one place since he left England. Hunt motioned to the different groups and explained, "Our fellow novices. We do the work in the kitchen, house and garden. You will have your duties assigned. Doubtless it will take you a little while to grow accustomed to the noise.

"If you will come in here," he continued, opening the door of a bleak room furnished with a plain table and some benches, "I shall obey Father Rector and give you an outline of what is expected of novices. I have been here only six months, and am not attempting to teach you. Father Rector delegated me because I am your countryman. Shall we sit down?"

They seated themselves on benches beside the table. Southwell noticed how the light from a high window revealed Hunt's plain face. While listening to the list of duties of the candidates for the Society of Jesus, Southwell realized that now at last he was enrolled and listening to a matter-of-fact description of the life for which he had longed. He felt the chill of the room, and heard the clatter of kettles and pans in the kitchen. Was this the heroic life of which he had dreamed? Was this the way to prepare for a mission to his homeland? Everything seemed so unromantic, so much nearer the pantry than the pulpit, nearer the scullery than the scaffold. He mustered his straying thoughts and listened. Most of what he heard he had heard many times before but now he, Robert Southwell, was one of the novices being described.

Hunt told the group that the novices of the Society of Jesus adhered to the same rule wherever they were. They were admitted if the Superiors found their answers to certain questions entirely satisfactory. They were not qualified if they had dependents, had ever belonged to a religious order, or had been unduly influenced to be Jesuits. They had to evidence stability, intelligence and that obedience considered essential to the life of the Society. Ignatius Loyola, a soldier by training, had formed his followers into what he called a "Company" and members of that company were supposed to obey their Superiors from the Pope down. The postulants, a name given to men who wished to be novices, were asked:

Are you willing to renounce the world, all possessions and all hope of temporal goods? Are you ready if necessary to beg your bread from door to door for the love of Jesus Christ? Are you ready to reside in any country and embrace any employment where your Superiors may think you to be most useful to the Glory of God and the good of souls? Are you willing to obey in all things in which there is evidently no sin, the Superiors who hold toward you the place of God? Do you feel resolved generally to renounce without reserve all those things which men in general love and embrace, and will you attempt and desire with all your strength what Our Lord Jesus Christ loved and embraced? Do you consent to put on the livery of humiliation worn by Him, to suffer as He did, and for love of Him, contempt, calumnies and insults?

The Constitutions and rules were explained and they were advised that the next two years were to be spent in the study of themselves and the formation of their characters rather than in the study of books.

Simon Hunt rose. Southwell and the others followed him out of the chilly room and all spent a few minutes together in the novitiate garden. In contrast with the air of the low-lying neighborhood of the Campus Martius where the English College stood, that on the Quirinal Hill was clear and fresh. Southwell breathed deep, and his country-trained eye took in the trees that were new to him, the live-oaks and olives. He noted the October roses blooming on the high stone wall, and he began to make a verse:

Then crop the morning rose while it is fair. . . .

This was a pleasant place and he liked it. He would write many poems.

But a novitiate was no place for poets. After an early afternoon dinner, he discovered that the life of a novice might require more heroism than he had anticipated, for he was set to work scrubbing a greasy pot. Hot water was not abundant; ordinary lye and sand the only abrasives to be had. He went at the job with a will, but without great aptitude. When at last the pot was clean, he regarded his hands ruefully. Swollen red fingers, a broken nail or two and scraped knuckles met his eyes. This was a matter for resolution, an occasion of which to remind himself, so he made an entry about his soul and God's knowledge of it in his spiritual notebook. . . . "He knows your gifts of nature and grace, and He has decided that the kitchen is the place that suits you best, at least, for the moment, though of course there may be needs in the future for which He will provide a different set of circumstances."

The notebook in which Southwell described some of his difficulties received many an entry during the next year. To record his failures helped him to face himself and overcome them. And, articulate, it was natural for him to put his thoughts on religion into words. It was not long before the entries in his pages showed that he was learning to pray as Ignatius Loyola had taught his followers in his book *The Spiritual Exercises*.

Southwell's strong will and vivid imagination aided him in avoiding vague, dreamy meditation. He put his mind on the subject that he was to consider. His prayer, which was all for the greater glory of God rather than for his own pleasure,

40

began when he placed himself in God's presence, continued when he called to mind a scene in the life of Our Lord. He made "a composition of place" picturing Our Lord's whereabouts; then he thought of how He looked, of how His companions looked, of what Jesus said and what others answered. He considered what he could learn from all of this, and when the time for prayer drew to an end, he made a "Colloquy" with petitions for greater understanding and love and for his personal needs. Then he always ended with an *Our Father*.

Southwell meditated especially on the mysteries of the Hidden Life of Our Lord and on the scenes of His Passion, and these became so much a part of his thoughts that presently he found himself thinking of them outside of the chapel and making them the subjects of little poems. After meditating on the Blessed Mother and the Baby Jesus and the coming of the Wise Men, he wrote:

> Three gifts they bring, three gifts they bear away.
> For incense, myrrh and gold, faith, hope and love.
> And with their gifts, the givers' hearts do stay,
> Their mind from Christ no parting can remove.

But whether he was scrubbing pots in the kitchen, sweeping the corridors, or kneeling in the chapel, Southwell was making ready to serve God as a Jesuit missioner and to be a martyr if God so willed. And he had a firm belief that, in order to be a successful missioner, he must have what he called "religious good manners." He wrote about this in his notebook, telling how he thought that courtesy attracted vocations. He made a resolution to be polite under all circumstances, and he held to it so firmly that he was remarkable for friendliness and serenity.

From the Novitiate of Sant' Andrea on the Quirinal Hill, Southwell moved the next year to the Roman College, then at the foot of the Capitoline. He was still a novice, but he was transferred to that institution that Ignatius Loyola had founded in order to study philosophy. There, there were learned professors and students of many nations. Father Robert Persons had charge of the English novices in the Roman College, and he took a special interest in Southwell.

The young Englishman, like his compatriots, had been schooled in the classics. Now, at the Roman College, he was living in the part of the city that the ancient Romans knew. When the students took walks, they passed the Tarpeian Rock, strolled by the Arch of Septimius Severus and into the Roman Forum. They scrambled through the ruins of the Palace of the Caesars on the Palatine, or visited the Circus Maximus or the Colosseum.

The Colosseum, open to the blue Italian sky, was a favorite place with the English. They explored the subterranean rooms where the wild animals used to be kept until let out for the Roman spectacles, or climbed into the crumbling galleries, or lingered near the cross erected on a level spot, and there considered the Christian martyrs who had suffered for the sport of the pagan emperors. For Southwell, there was always the thought that if he ever reached England, he might also suffer. And always he prayed that he would be brave.

One holiday, Father Persons and Southwell were sitting on an overturned column in the Colosseum. The sun was pleasantly warm, and tiny lizards slid up from among the acanthus leaves and the yellow mustard flowers and stretched themselves on the gray rocks. Swallows circled overhead, and little children darted from one hiding place to another, their voices full of laughter.

Presently Father Persons exclaimed, "How peaceful! One wouldn't think that this was ever the scene of bloodshed."

Southwell looked up. "I was thinking just that, Father. I was wondering if it is wrong to want to be a martyr."

"Why wrong?" asked the older man.

"Because . . . well, I was thinking about England. I would be glad to die for our Faith, but I would be sorry for our countrymen to be guilty of my death."

Father Persons replied, "Perhaps you think too much about martyrdom, Robert. You know that you can live for your Faith as well as die for it. Look at the man approaching us from that furthest archway to our left. He looks strong enough to be a gladiator, doesn't he? Well, wait a minute and you will see that he is an Englishman, and, if I am not mistaken, one whom I know."

The tall, athletic man swung toward them. Recognizing Father Persons, he hurried his steps. "Father!" he said. "They told me at the College that I might find you here."

"Gilbert!" exclaimed Father Persons.

The two shook hands, and Southwell, having been introduced, dropped shyly into the background and looked with wonder on George Gilbert, whom Father Darbyshire had converted when he was at the French Court. Southwell noticed the newcomer's hesitant speech that contrasted so oddly with the self-confident bearing of a man already in possession of a large inheritance. Here was a leader, he thought, a young man whom others would love and trust and follow, a generous person who would give unstintingly of his strength and money.

"How is my former Protestant and Puritan?" asked Father Persons.

"A little weak in the knees," replied Gilbert, laughing. "His Holiness has sent for me; he wants news of England from where I have just come. I never expected to confer with a Pope!"

"You will not feel shy with Pope Gregory. He has the cause of England at heart. Perhaps he will want you to return there. Converts like you know how to deal with those who do not belong to the Church."

"Perhaps. I am certain that Dr. Allen and Dr. Gregory Martin are right in thinking that the English translation of the Bible must be published for Catholics. The uneducated English do not read Latin, and the Protestants claim that the Church keeps the Scriptures hidden from the people."

"Dr. Martin has gone far with the translation," said Father Persons, "but the cost of printing will be great. And because of heavy fines for attending Mass, many of the English Catholics are poor."

"A fortune might be worse spent than on such a publishing venture," said Gilbert. "By the way, I understand that there have been changes at the Roman English College since Dr. Gregory Martin returned to France."

Father Persons looked up quickly. "Yes, some of the older students felt that the Warden was letting the College become little more than a residence for the English and Welsh. They wanted to be trained for the missions, and when they could not get an interview with the Cardinal Protector Farnese, they decided to leave. They packed up and quit, but before setting out for France, they went over to the Vatican. The Pope was in Saint Peter's inspecting a new altar. They were brave enough to put the matter before him. Well, the result was their return to the College, which is to be under the care of the Jesuits. I imagine that Father Alphonsus Agazzari, who will be Rector, will be strict enough to please Sherwin. And every student there is to take the College Oath."

"Yes. I saw Sherwin's in the new Diary: 'Ralph Sherwin, English, a priest, aged 29, a student of Sacred Theology, declares and swears upon the Holy Scriptures, that he is ready today rather than tomorrow, at the intimation of Superiors, to proceed to England for the help of souls.' There is a man for you, Father. No nonsense about Sherwin!"

Southwell, listening, agreed with all his heart.

"But will there be no Jesuits going to England?" asked Gilbert.

"We do not know. We Jesuits go or stay wherever the Pope and our Father General command," replied Father Persons. "But you will come to the Roman College and dine with us before your audience with His Holiness?"

"Yes. I had expected you to fortify me," answered Gilbert. "Indeed, I thought that you might coach me a bit in Vatican manners. There is still a touch of the Protestant in my behavior."

As they walked through the Forum to the Roman College, Southwell kept a few paces behind. He was thinking that these men were different from the Catholics who frequented the English Court. Their attitude was more aggressive. Neither Gilbert nor Persons was a born aristocrat as he and Dr. Allen were. Then a wave of homesickness swept over him. What was the news of his family? While he was in France he had occasionally had word through the Copleys. Here he had no kinsman save Sir Richard Shelley, who had been away from England for years.

Chapter 7

It was spring. The peach trees had blossomed on the Aventine Hill, and now the acacias were in golden bloom on the Palatine. The Roman Forum was sprinkled with white daisies and alyssum. Lent, with its visits to various station churches associated with the saints, had passed. Easter had come and the English in Rome had taken part in its ceremonies.

The English were in a state of excitement, for Bishop Thomas Goldwell, the very old English prelate who had refused to take the Oath of Supremacy when Elizabeth came to the throne, and Dr. Nicholas Morton, Canon Penitentiary of Saint Peter's, were about to set out for England, which was without any Bishop to confirm the children or make decisions for the clergy. Father Ralph Sherwin was to go with them. Father Robert Persons and the clever Jesuit classicist Father Edmund Campion, accompanied by the tiny Jesuit lay brother Ralph Emerson, were also of the party. The Father General of the Society of Jesus had agreed to Dr. Allen's request that a few Jesuits go to England.

Nobody was more excited that Easter Week of 1580 than Southwell. He was young and unimportant, but there was no detail in the arrangements that did not interest him. The Bishop, who was eighty years old, was to ride ahead with Dr. Morton. The others were to walk across Italy and through the Alps to France, where they would secretly board ships for England. They had a pack horse to carry their belongings.

Southwell would miss Sherwin and Father Persons, but he was happy to think that they would have Edmund Campion for a companion. Campion was brilliant and gay and holy. As a boy, he had been to Christ Hospital School in London; he had been chosen from all the scholars there to make a Latin speech of welcome to Queen Mary Tudor. Later, he had gone to Saint John's College, Oxford, and when Queen Elizabeth and Sir William Cecil, the Prime Minister, visited there, he represented the University and welcomed the Sovereign and her favorite, the Earl of Leicester. He was popular at Oxford and in Ireland where he went later. But the more he studied and read, the more certain he had become that he must be a

Catholic. He had been influenced, too, by Gregory Martin and Lord Vaux of Harrowden, whose small son Harry he had tutored. The upshot of it all was his going to Douay where he began his studies for the priesthood. From Douay he went to Rome, sought admission to the Society of Jesus, and now he had just returned from Prague in Bohemia where he had been ordained priest and had taught rhetoric. Sir Philip Sidney, the poet, had been to see him in Prague, for his Protestant friends still loved and admired him.

Campion and Persons were both clear thinkers, and they asked the Father General of the Society of Jesus and Pope Gregory XIII for explicit directions and permissions. They were told that, in spite of Pius V's Bull of Excommunication, loyal Catholics were to obey Queen Elizabeth in civil matters as long as she remained Queen of England in fact, if not by right, and that it would be their duty to strengthen the faith of Catholics by administering the Sacraments: that they were not expected to try to convert Protestants. They were expressly commanded to avoid politics. Pope Gregory received them in audience and made a contribution to defray the expense of the journey.

Before leaving Rome, Sherwin sought out his old friend Father Philip Neri. He knelt for Father Philip's blessing, and initiated a custom that became dear to the missioners, who thereafter were loathe to leave without the benediction of the Apostle of Rome, who had so long foreseen their martyrdom.

The day set for the priests' departure was April 18. Southwell joined his kinsman Sir Richard Shelley and the other English who lived in Rome, and accompanied the group out the Flaminian Way to the Milvian Bridge. Along the route, white rambler roses tumbled over ancient gray walls. When they reached the Tiber, they looked across its yellow sand banks to the nearby hills and the distant blue mountains.

Sir Richard Shelley was in a somber mood. "They could not have chosen a worse time," he said to Southwell. "Sir Francis Walsingham has some excuse for suspecting travelers from Rome to England. And his spy system, which is the best in the world, is already alerted. I'll wager spies are forwarding descriptions of Campion this very minute."

Southwell looked at Campion who, like the rest of the company, had left off clerical dress for the journey. He had named himself "Mr. Patrick" and was got up as a serving man in an old buckram suit and a worn cloak. He was as merry as could be, and contrasted oddly with serious Persons and Sherwin and small Ralph Emerson. "I think, sir," replied Southwell, "that their disguises are well chosen."

"Bosh!" said Sir Richard. "A priest in layman's attire is always awkward. And a Jesuit might as well have the word written on his face. You are beginning to get the look yourself. Control, restraint, silence leave their mark."

Southwell smiled inwardly. He was not known for silence. He knew that Sir Richard expected to miss Father Persons and hated to see him leave. Hoping to pacify his granduncle, he said, "Our Fathers will find a good friend in George Gilbert if they reach London. He has organized unmarried Catholic gentlemen who dare to help priests in England."

"Yes, so I hear. And Campion will have a fine ally in Lord William Vaux, and in young Harry, whose tutor he was. They are kinsmen of yours, by the way. Come, let's bid the travelers farewell and get back to the city." He led Southwell to say good-bye to Persons, who had been his confessor, and to Sherwin, who had been his mentor and friend. Southwell had a lump in his throat when he returned to the Roman College to work hard at theology.

For weeks, he waited eagerly for news of the travelers, for he knew that he could count on their writing letters that the

English in Rome would share. Finally, when the city was enveloped in the summer heat, letters came from Campion and Sherwin. The group had journeyed to Florence, Milan, and by way of Geneva to Rheims. There old Bishop Goldwell gave up, thinking himself too old and weak to proceed. As a result, England was left without a bishop for many years. But Campion, Persons and little Ralph Emerson went from Rheims to the Jesuit house at St. Omer, and Sherwin took his pupil Pascal and went to Rouen where his uncle was living. It was easy to reach Channel ports from Rouen and St. Omer.

At St. Omer, Father Persons decided to go on to England, and bade Campion and Ralph Emerson wait in France until they had word from him.

Southwell, Matthew Marshall and George Haydock could scarcely restrain their excitement when they first learned the contents of Campion's letter to the Father General, who was then in Rome. It read in part: "Father Robert sailed from Calais after midnight. . . . They got him up like a soldier: such a peacock! such a swaggerer, such duds, such a glance, such a strut! A man would need a sharp eye to glimpse the holiness and modesty that lurk underneath it all." Campion explained that he and the small lay brother were to dress up also, "to cheat the madness of the world." Emerson was to be disguised as Campion's servant, for it was thus that two traveled together when possible, one seeming to be master, the other valet.

Soon news came that Campion and Ralph Emerson had gone on to London, and that George Gilbert had taken lodgings for them in the house of the Chief Pursuivant in Chancery Lane.

Ralph Sherwin's letter was to Father Agazzari of the English College. He told of the clerics' journey, "I do not like to say in what straits we were placed, but they were very great indeed, and we hope that the Pope will be informed of it at a fitting opportunity, in order that the others may be better provided for. Not double what we received for traveling expenses would be really sufficient. . . ."

"Good old Sherwin!" exclaimed Southwell and Haydock when they heard this. "He is always thinking of the needs of missioners."

"Yes," said Marshall, "he thinks that if the Pope understood how costly it is for Englishmen to travel, he would hand out more money."

In a letter to his friends in Rome who had been at Oxford with him, Sherwin wrote that he had had word that their Alma Mater was wholly corrupted, and continued, "I commend myself to all of you whose company, to my consolation, I hope to enjoy in Heaven. And I ask your prayers."

When Sherwin wrote, his visit to his uncle was almost at an end, and on June 11, 1580, he wrote from Paris, "Even while I penned these letters, Mr. Pascal came with the frip to frenchify me. God give us still priests' minds, for we go far astray from the habit here. Mr. Pascal says, 'You will never be handsome!' and I tell him there was never a priest handsome in such attire. . . . Thus for Christ, we put ourselves in colors."

Southwell, listening to the letter, imagined how Sherwin looked in bright silk and velvet, a starched ruff, a slashed doublet, trunk hose padded to make his legs fashionably large, and carrying a plumed hat and flashing sword. It was like him to buy his garb from a fripper, a dealer in second-hand clothes. And probably some disguise was advisable, for had he worn the old cassock which he had worn when he received Father Philip's blessing, Sir Francis Walsingham's spies would have followed him to the channel ship and he would not have reached England. But if ever a man looked the priest, it was Sherwin, and Southwell found himself thinking that Sir Richard Shelley was a wise old man.

The year 1580 was rich in letters, and Southwell's ability as a writer was evident in his replies. One letter to which he responded with delight came in the autumn. It was from his friend John Deckers, who was in the Jesuit Novitiate in Naples, and who had not been able to see Southwell when he had passed through Rome some months prior to writing. In it, he recalled that Southwell had been braver than he and had gone on across the Alps before he dared.

Southwell answered, reminding Deckers of their first meeting in Douay, and of the progress of their acquaintance: "No friend was then so dear to John as Robert, none so dear to Robert as John. No delight in this world seemed greater than to enter into the Society. Not a day passed, not an opportunity was lost. Whatever free time we could find for our conversation together seemed all too short. . . . As then Jesus Christ laid the foundation of our fellowship (and on this point I have not the slightest doubt), and the desire we both shared of serving Him was the force that consolidated our union in its progress, why should not the result we both longed for consummate our friendship?"

In other words, to be Jesuits together would be great happiness. This came to pass when John Deckers arrived from Naples and became Southwell's fellow student at the great Roman College. But even before his friend joined him, Southwell took a further step in the Society of Jesus on which they had set their youthful hearts. On the Feast of Saint Luke, October 18, 1580, he took the simple vows of a Jesuit Scholastic.

Chapter 8

Just enough light entered the room to reveal a fair thin man lying on a bed and an auburn-haired man writing at a table by a heavily curtained window.

"How do you feel, Haydock?" asked Southwell.

"Ill, thank you," replied George Haydock. "It is almost the hour for my chill, you know. I was lying here thinking of all that has happened in England since we left. I wish I could have seen Sir Francis Drake bring the *Golden Hind* into Plymouth last September when he had completed his voyage around the world."

"I wish so, too. A Puritan, and something of a pirate, but a great navigator. The Queen herself went aboard the ship, they say."

"It is time for news from home again," said Haydock. "We haven't had word in a long time. What are you writing? Since you came out with honors in your disputation in Philosophy at the Roman College and came over here to the English College to live, you are forever writing."

"A habit of mine," replied Southwell, laying his pen aside.

"John Deckers said that yours was the most brilliant Public Defense ever heard at the College," continued Haydock. "Tell me about it. I need to be diverted. Or read me what you have written in that notebook."

Southwell smiled. "I have written some advice for myself in

case I should be ill again. I was with Nicholas Smith when he was ill before they sent him back to France. And I saw poor Matthew Marshall suffer until he died in February. God rest his soul."

"And now you are nursing George Haydock, who has malaria or quartan fever or the ague. Whatever the physicians call it, you and I know the symptoms. But read. Maybe I'll profit by your counsel. Have the blankets handy, though. I think the chill will soon be here."

Southwell piled some blankets on a chair near the bed, and then shyly and rapidly read what he had written: "In sickness, I must keep my expression serene and cheerful rather than sad. I must ask for nothing forbidden by the physician or that is in any way hurtful. I must eat what is given me as nearly as I can. If disinclined to food, I may say so, but if I am ordered to eat I must consume as much as I can without impatience. I must make no unnecessary demand or rejection."

"Good!" exclaimed Haydock. "And finished on the minute. Here is my chill! Pray for me. I remember that much of your counsel. And the blankets, please."

Southwell approached the bed, and taking the blankets, began to tuck them about Haydock, who clutched them around his shoulders with shaking hands. Suddenly, his face and lips were blue, and he shivered from head to foot and lay in an agony of cold. "This is the hardest part," he managed to say, his teeth chattering. "The chill is worse than the fever. Is there another blanket?"

Southwell found another blanket and spread it carefully over his patient, then sat beside him on a stool and thought about this Roman malady that afflicted so many of the English students. Like the Romans, he thought the bad air in the low parts of the city accountable, and he knew that attacks came on sometimes after an infected person had been in the sun. Time and again, he had heard the Romans warn the English to walk in the shade.

Now he looked on Haydock with great pity, every now and then tucking the blankets tighter, or rising to draw the blind so that the light would not be in the sick man's eyes.

The door opened, and a sly-faced, sloe-eyed student stepped in. "On the rack already, Haydock? Practicing for martyrdom, no doubt. Well, your friend Father Sherwin is further along the way." Anthony Munday walked over to a table, chose an orange from a plate, and began to peel it for himself.

"A dispatch has come from England?" asked Southwell gently, motioning to Haydock, whose chill was at its height and who was shaking like a leaf.

"Yes. And I thought I'd be your little Mercury and bring the good news of your hero. Arrested in November and put in the Marshalsea Prison. Taken to the Tower, racked, and laid out in the snow to die. But he didn't. He was still a Tower prisoner when the newsletter was written. Fool! All he needed to do was to—"

A sudden movement on the bed attracted Southwell's attention. Haydock's face was no longer blue with chill, but red with fever, and he was beginning to shove the blankets off with his hot hands and to thrash about on the bed.

Southwell turned to the caller. "Thank you for coming. I wonder if you would go the refectory and request someone to bring Haydock a drink."

"Mercury dismissed on an errand of mercy," said Munday. "Gifford and I are forever being reminded that we live among saints."

Munday went out, and Southwell took Haydock's wrist and found that his pulse was too rapid to count. The patient's flushed face was quite cheerful, however. "It is good to be warm again," he remarked. "And without a visitor. Sometimes I wonder if Munday is a spy—"

"Don't try to talk," interrupted Southwell, putting his hand on Haydock's hot forehead.

Haydock closed his eyes and both men remained silent for some time. Presently beads of perspiration appeared on Haydock's brow, his fair hair became damp and his thin hands clammy. "Ah, here is the sweat. And you may not believe it possible after what we just heard about good old Sherwin, but I believe I am going to sleep."

Southwell folded all the blankets save a light one that he spread over the emaciated form.

"Another bout over," said Haydock drowsily. "Intermittent fever! We can expect another attack Thursday. They made you Repetitor here at the College to help us students with our lessons, not to nurse our ague. Thank you. Good old Sherwin will be praying for us in the Tower. If he isn't already in Heaven."

Southwell patted Haydock's shoulder affectionately, then went out, closing the door behind him. He was thinking that the Superiors would not let the sick student remain through the hot Roman summer. He was almost ready for ordination, but they would send him on to France and let him be made priest there. Dr. Gregory Martin had returned to Rheims, and there would be other friends to greet him.

Then Southwell sped down the stairs that he had first climbed with Sherwin, and went into the small church. There he had prayed with Sherwin the night that he arrived in Rome, and now he offered the prayer that he had used then, the *Suscipe,* and added to it Sherwin's favorite ejaculation, Jesus, Jesus, Jesus, be my Saviour.

Chapter 9

On December 2, 1581, Southwell took the English College Oath. "Robert Southwell, English, aged 20, a student of sacred theology, declares and swears upon the Holy Scriptures that he is willing, at the intimation of Superiors, to proceed to England for the help of souls." He wondered how long it would be before he actually returned to his native land. He was only twenty years old, not old enough to be ordained, and although he already had his bachelor's degree, he had years of study ahead. Years, too, it would seem, of humdrum routine at the College, counseling the other students and helping them with their lessons. George Haydock had gone north to Rheims because of his health. Anthony Munday had quit, and Gifford had been expelled, but there were still students who, although not bad like Gifford and Munday, loved their ease and were not preparing themselves for the missionary life. These presented a problem, but Southwell, struggling for peace among them, held himself in check and maintained the serenity that he knew to be important.

Now and then, there would be a trickle of news from England. He would hear of the enormous fines that his cousin George Cotton of Warblington was paying the Government, or of the result of some of his Uncle Thomas Copley's schemes to keep his estate intact. But there was never a word from his father and brothers, and he wrote Father Persons and asked him to try to strengthen them in the Faith. About Sherwin, there was merely the confirmation that he was alive and in the Tower. Because of the well-planned Jesuit letters, there was news of Father Persons and Father Campion and the great work they were doing, riding from manor to manor, saying Mass and hearing confessions. It was common knowledge that George Gilbert's association of Catholic laymen made this possible. Thanks to Gilbert, Harry Vaux and other friends, there were always horses and escorts for the Jesuits, and an invariable welcome in the homes of the Catholic gentry. Word had come that Campion had written and secretly printed a Latin book, *Rationes Decem*. His purpose was to explain the reasons for being a Catholic.

On the whole, however, news was scant, not enough to distract Southwell from his studies at the Roman College or his duties at the English College, except occasionally when he took to writing newsletters relaying these reports from England.

There were many cold, gray days that winter, drizzly days when the damp air chilled the students to the bones as they walked to and from their classes. Southwell shivered in huge rooms dependent for heat on *scaldini,* small iron pots in which live coals were stowed. He was as thankful as the other students when darkness fell and they could gather before a fire in the hall for evening recreation.

One windy night, the English were sitting close to the hearth watching the glow of burning pine cones and olive-tree roots and wishing for a fire of giant oak logs such as they would have had at home. Suddenly, they were aware of commotion in the corridor outside. Doors were being opened and closed. Heavy steps sounded on the stone floor, and a familiar voice came to them. Someone started up, exclaiming, "Why, that is

George Gilbert's voice. I would know its booming and stuttering anywhere!"

"Gilbert! George Gilbert!" came as a chorus from the others. "Gilbert in Rome? How can that be?"

The door opened and the tall man strode into the room.

"Gilbert," the students cried, rushing to him and wringing his hand. "What of Father Ralph? Father Edmund?"

"In Heaven," was the reply. "Hanged, drawn, and quartered at Tyburn on the first of December. With them died Father Alexander Briant." He drew something from his pocket and held it up for all to see. "This is a cross that Briant whittled when he was in prison. He carried it to the scaffold with him. A bystander obtained it for me."

They looked with awe on the memento of a martyr, then grouped themselves around Gilbert, who had dropped into a chair by the fire.

"You mean to tell us that Campion, Sherwin and Briant are martyrs?"

"Yes. And Sherwin is your proto-martyr: the first man from this English College to give his life for the Faith."

"Good old Sherwin," muttered someone. "Steady, always steady."

"He was to the end," Gilbert assured them.

"And Father Persons?" demanded Southwell.

"He had to leave England secretly. He was so much sought that his presence endangered any household that sheltered him. The same of me. Wherever we went to spend even one night, our host and hostess and their families risked searchers and imprisonment. I am not easily concealed, you know."

"And Brother Ralph Emerson?"

"Too small to martyr," laughed Gilbert. "He was invaluable to Campion as messenger and aide. He blames himself for letting Father Edmund send him off on an errand, for he thinks that, had he been there at Lyford Grange where

Campion preached and celebrated Mass, the latter would not have been captured."

"You were never caught yourself?" an eager voice asked.

"No. A number of us unmarried men devoted our time to helping priests. I hired rooms in the Chief Pursuivant's house, thinking it a good plan to live near him and keep an eye on the scoundrel. We had many of Sir Francis Walsingham's men in our pay. Some of the searchers are former highwaymen and criminals, and we had at least as good a chance as Sir Francis to get honest service from them. We found Catholic families so desirous of hearing Mass and going to Holy Communion that they were willing to receive priests in their houses. We had hiding holes built; we kept horses ready for the priests' journeys, and ourselves accompanied them from manor to manor. A great life!"

"What about the book that Father Campion wrote?" asked Southwell, always interested in books.

"Oh, there's a tale! The ladies who are recusants are not afraid of anything. One of them, Dame Cecily Stonor, let Father Persons set up a printing press at her house near Henley. Another recusant agreed to get the book printed, and got horses and fine clothes for the printers who, of course, had to pose as gentlemen visiting Dame Cecily's house. I supplied machinery, type, paper, the prosaic parts. We could not get sufficient type, so the work was slow. Campion himself saw the book through the press, and that daring Father Hartley took copies to Oxford and placed them on the benches in Saint Mary's on June 27, just in time for Commencement! What a success it was! Everybody read Campion's wonderful Latin instead of attending to the Commencement exercises. On the whole, we had a grand, exciting time."

"And Dr. Gregory Martin's New Testament? Any news of that?" asked Southwell.

"My lad, you anticipate. But there will be news. My men

will smuggle copies of the new Bible in by way of a creek near Arundel Castle. They have been printed at Rheims."

"Was the printing costly?" asked Southwell.

"I had a letter from Dr. Allen saying that he had hoped to get the edition printed for 1000 crowns and it cost 1500. A habit books have."

Southwell caught Gilbert's eye, and the latter looked away. "A fortune might be worse spent than on such a publishing venture," came as an echo.

Just then Father Rector Agazzari came in, and everyone rose. A student poked the fire, and as the men seated themselves again, the light played on Gilbert's face and revealed its expression of weariness and emotion.

"Would it tire you too much to tell us what happened after Father Campion's arrest?" inquired Father Rector.

"I could talk about it all night," Gilbert assured him. "There were four priests arrested at a country house, Lyford Grange, and conducted to London. They were strapped on their horses. Campion was in the lead. There was a paper on his hat bearing the words 'Campion the Seditious Jesuit.' They went through crowded streets to the Tower and were taken into custody by Sir Owen Hopton, the Governor." Everyone in the room listened breathlessly. "Yes, you have guessed right: Father Campion was put into Little Ease, one of the worst of the small dungeons. For four days he was confined there without room to stand up or lie down. After that, he was taken by boat to the Earl of Leicester's town house, where were Bedford, Lord Burghley, Sir Francis Walsingham, and Her Majesty, Queen Elizabeth. I think they hoped he would recant in such fine company. Needless to say, he stood firm. For three days after, everything was done to flatter him into conforming. The news was spread that he would give up his Catholic religion. When he refused, he was fastened to the rollers of the Tower rack

60

and tortured. All the while, he was questioned about where he had said Mass, whose confessions he had heard. His movements had been so closely watched that Walsingham knew the answers to these questions. Names of the very persons he had absolved were given out as having been mentioned by Campion. London was scandalized. Campion was said to be a coward and a knave! There was a public disputation in the Norman Chapel of the Tower. Campion faced the questioning divines. He had no books of reference. He sat on a low stool. Truly, he reminded one of poor Joan of Arc at Rouen.

"That was the first conference. There were others all through the autumn. He was racked again until his arms and legs were numb. Walsingham thought up a silly plot, and pretended that Campion had attempted to raise a sedition and assassinate the Queen. He and eight others, including your own Ralph Sherwin, were arraigned in Westminster Hall November 14. When they were tried for high treason, November 20, Ralph Sherwin called out, 'The plain ground of our standing here is religion, not treason.' "

Gilbert paused, then continued, "Chief Justice Wray presided. Eliot, who arrested Campion, was a witness."

There was an uneasy stir among the students. They had been warned that Walsingham had paid spies in their midst. Could there have been one here, a companion, who denounced their well-loved Sherwin?

"Campion was superb in his defense," explained Gilbert. "The chief count against him was that he would not take the Oath of Supremacy. His answers were unflinching. He repeated the replies he had given Her Majesty when questioned at the Earl of Leicester's house. '. . . I acknowledge Her Majesty as my governor and sovereign; I acknowledge Her Majesty both in fact and by right to be Queen; I confess an obedience due to the Crown as my temporal head and primate. . . . I will willingly pay to Her Majesty what is hers; yet I must pay to God what is His.' "

Gilbert paused again. Someone passed him a cup, but he pushed it aside with a word of thanks, and continued, "Once Campion cried out that if religion made them traitors, they were worthy to be condemned."

"Religion is what Ralph Sherwin said they were condemned for," an excited student broke in.

"Just that," said Gilbert. He turned to Father Agazzari, "You know the rest, Father Rector. They were condemned and clapped close prisoners in the Tower. Father Briant, a man with a face like an angel, was to die with them." Gilbert held up the small cross. "Pass it around," he suggested.

Student after student handled and examined the cross that Briant had whittled in his cell, and on which he had drawn in charcoal a figure of Our Saviour. The cross reached Southwell, and he held it while Gilbert continued. "The three were bound to hurdles at the Tower gates. It was rainy. They were dragged through Cheapside, Newgate Street, Holborn to Tyburn. Oh, Father Rector! You know what their prayers were, their glorious faith, their courage."

"Yes," said Father Agazzari, rising. "All of you come to the chapel for a *Te Deum*."

As the others started, Gilbert stepped back to Southwell, who handed him Briant's cross. Their eyes met. "Probably I shall not live to die at Tyburn. But you will, Southwell. Do you think that Father Rector would agree to my having our martyrs' portraits painted on the chapel walls?"

"Yes. You have funds left?"

"Enough for that. My estates were confiscated. But I need nothing; I am to enter the Society of Jesus . . . if I live to enter."

George Gilbert commissioned an artist to paint the martyrs'

portraits in the chapel. Then, weary but determined, he became a Jesuit novice at Sant' Andrea.

Southwell watched the progress of the painting. From season to season more martyrs were added to the College list: Luke Kirby, John Shert and others. These were men whom he had known, and for one of his years to associate the pictures of his friends with their last words on the scaffold was a strange experience.

Southwell, acting as Repetitor, in charge of tutorial work among the younger students, felt the seriousness of preparing them to be as brave as the first English College alumni had been. Often, walking with the students two by two to the Roman College for classes, or laughing with them in the garden during recreation, he prayed that whatever he did would strengthen them for trial. Some of them were very young, and although Dr. Allen and Father Persons forever warned that very young men must not be sent on the English mission, there was a temptation to the Superiors to send them, for they were eager to go and the need for priests in England was great.

Father Persons had had to seek refuge on the Continent and was never to return to England again. Southwell's cousin George Cotton was in Fleet Prison. In the Marshalsea Prison the recusants had contrived to hide missals and altar vessels and have Mass celebrated secretly in their cells. And very sad news came from Rheims: Dr. Gregory Martin, his translation of the Old Testament and the New Testament completed, had died of tuberculosis. When in the autumn of 1583 George Gilbert died in the novitiate in Rome with Father Briant's cross clasped in his hand, Southwell felt that many of his most cherished friends were in Heaven. Fortunately, some of his English friends had come to Rome. And John Deckers was still there.

Chapter 10

The weather was warm, and as the students trudged to the Roman College for their classes, Southwell did not have to remind them to walk in the shade, as he had all winter. He noticed that even the newly arrived Christopher Bales and Christopher Buxton avoided the sun. Bales, a zealous, forthright young man, was from Durham. Buxton, gay and outspoken, was a Derbyshire man.

A dispatch had arrived just as they set out. There was a letter for Southwell but he could not stop to read it. His class seemed very long to him. As he listened to his professor, he thought that he must sit through dinner with an eye on the younger students and then share their recreation before he would be free to read his letter. He had asked Father Rector to glance through it in his absence.

It was a half-holiday, and when recreation was over, he sent Bales and Buxton to make themselves ready for a call on Father Philip Neri, who had moved to the Chiesa Nuova. Then he went to Father Agazzari for his letter.

The compassionate Jesuit held it out to him, remarking gently, "Another one of ours in Heaven. Our George."

"George Haydock!" exclaimed Southwell, and his mind harked back to the thin, fair man lying on a bed in a darkened room.

"And it will distress you to know that when George was

about to be executed, Anthony Munday pushed his way through the crowd to the scaffold, and shouted, 'I heard him say in Rome that he would like to kill the Queen!' Poor Munday. I was always fearful for him; he was ever unruly."

Southwell was standing like one stunned, the letter in his hand.

"Does it make you feel very old and responsible to have the account of a martyrdom addressed to you?" asked Father Rector, kindly. "You will be glad to know that, although Haydock had been seven months in solitary confinement, he was put into free custody in the Tower, and contrived to minister to his fellow prisoners, hearing their confessions. His fever had returned, and they took pity on him and gave him some liberty. Father Philip called on his way back to the Chiesa Nuova and said that you were bringing Bales and Buxton to visit him. I suggest that you wait to read the letter until you get there. Haydock shared Father Philip's custom of visiting the Seven Churches. Sometimes I have thought that he contracted malaria on those excursions."

Southwell thanked Father Agazzari, and, as Bales and Buxton came at that moment, he plunged ahead so fast that they could not keep up. His face was drawn and white as he strode through the Campo dei Fiori, giving no attention to the bustling shoppers fresh from their siesta, or to the hucksters crying their wares. Lithe, slim, always a rapid walker, he went through the crowded market place without pausing, whereas his companions jostled and were jostled and were impeded by basket-laden donkeys goaded by tanned peasants.

"Is it far?" panted Buxton, catching up with Southwell at last as they neared the Chiesa Nuova.

"No. There it is. The large new building ahead, Santa Maria in Vallicella."

The three entered the church and prayed a minute before

the tabernacle. A lad, evidently stationed at a side door to escort them, beckoned. They followed him into an adjoining building and up long stairs to Father Philip's apartment, which was at the very top, looking out over Rome itself and the green Janiculum Hill. The lad knocked, and at Father Philip's word opened the door and admitted them.

The old priest laid aside his breviary and rose. When Southwell had presented Bales and Buxton, he asked, "The news from England is good?"

"The best," murmured Southwell, tears welling to his eyes. "One of ours. George Haydock. He behaved well."

"One of mine, too," said Father Philip. "He loved Rome as I do. I used to meet him making the visits to the Seven Churches. But he was often ill with malaria."

"He suffered frightfully with chills, but due to his illness, he was put into free custody in the Tower. Since that enabled him to hear the prisoners' confessions, he was doubtless thankful that he was a victim of the ague," said Southwell.

"Let's hear the letter," said Father Philip, seating himself and his guests, with Southwell close to a window so that he would have light to read.

As calmly as he could, Southwell read, translating the account into Latin so the Italian priest as well as the young Englishmen might understand. It was a letter from a man who had been present when George Haydock was executed February 12, 1584, and who, prior to that, had heard from his own lips about his experiences when examined by the Commissioners.

Haydock had been questioned about the Oath of the English College at Rome, and the reaction on the Continent to Father Campion's death. A paper had been shown to Haydock on which the names of English College students were written. At this point in the reading, Southwell looked up and saw how distressed young Bales and Buxton were. "That is usual," he explained. "Sir Francis Walsingham's spies know our names, our habits, our every move, and report to their master." Then he read the account of how George Haydock and four other Catholics were drawn from the Tower to Tyburn on hurdles, and of how Father Haydock recited in Latin the Evening Hymn of the Church as he climbed onto the cart beneath the gallows. Admonished to pray in English, he did not say that God understood Latin, as others had, but calmly continued. All the bystanders were impressed by his appearance, his fair complexion, mild countenance and determined bearing. He was told to ask the Queen's forgiveness. He protested that he was not guilty of treason and so would not ask pardon, and added, "I take her for my lawful Queen, and this morning have said many Our Fathers for her. I pray that she may long reign Queen. If I had her in the wilderness, I would not for all the world hurt her even with a pin prick."

"Ah," interrupted Father Philip. "I remember hearing that he was falsely accused of plotting against her, just as Campion was."

Southwell, holding the paper to the light, continued to read,

"He requested all Catholics to pray for him and his country.
'There are no Catholics here,' said a bystander.
'Yes,' said another, 'we are all Catholics.'
'I mean Catholics of the Catholic Roman Church, and I pray God that my blood may increase the Catholic faith in England.'"

Then the cart was driven away from under the gibbet, and Haydock hung by the rope. He was cut down while still living, and subjected to the final torture.

Southwell, lifting his eyes from the paper, saw that Bales' lips were trembling and that the knuckles of Buxton's clenched fists were white.

Father Philip noticed Southwell's sorrow and the young men's dismay. He reminded them, "Haydock had gone to England as a missioner. He was that when he heard confessions in the Tower. His vocation was fulfilled. He served God as he was called to do to the very end." Putting his hand on Bales' shoulder, and beckoning Southwell and Buxton, he conducted them to a short stair that led to a lookout, a sort of open gallery above the roof tops. "There is George Haydock's Rome," he said.

From the vantage point, the three Englishmen gazed on the ancient buildings golden in the late sunlight. Father Philip, beside them, was murmuring, "Beautiful Rome. Another martyr looks down on it from Heaven."

Chapter 11

It was May 1, 1585, the day of the crowning of Pope Sixtus V. Southwell, now an ordained priest, had taken advantage of the College holiday to spend an hour or two on the Janiculum Hill with his young cousin, Anthony Copley, who had come from England some months before.

Southwell had aged during the year. Soon to be appointed Prefect of Studies and Assistant to the Rector of the English College, he was facing new responsibilities. Already he was on friendly terms with the English refugees in Rome and with many of the learned men, including Father Henry Garnet, the Jesuit, who taught at the Roman College.

"Is Father Garnet going to England?" asked Copley, rising from their seat, which commanded a view of the still unfinished dome of Saint Peter's, and stretching himself on the ground. He braced his elbows, cupped his chin in his hands, and looked up at his cousin.

"Not this year, I think. He was to have joined Father Weston in London. But there has been a change of plans."

"Father Weston is forever in and out of prison," said Anthony. "He finds the Marshalsea and the Clink fertile ground for his labors; many recusants in them, and, of course, when you are in prison for your religion, you practice it." The speaker's dancing eyes challenged his cousin's priestly gravity.

"Tony! For all you know, your mother and sister may be confined for religion at this moment. They are faithful, and may have been arrested at Gatton. Since your father's death and my mother's, Aunt Katherine has a great burden in decisions for you young members of the family. I wish that I knew about my father and brothers."

"I tried to discover your father's attitude before I left. But he avoids your mother's religious relatives. It is very expensive to be a Catholic with so many fines to pay."

"Was there news of my brothers?"

"Dick stays pretty close to home, I think. But Tom is a gay bird. . . . They say that he offended Her Majesty by his attentions to a girl at court. Our Queen is fifty-two years old, but she thinks that she is the only girl in the world."

"Tony!" protested Southwell.

"It is true. She will not even speak to Countess Anne, Philip Howard's wife. Probably because she is pretty. By the way, Philip Howard is a Catholic now. After he saw how Father Campion behaved at his trial, he decided to be one. Father Weston brought him back into the Church last year."

"Good! What title has he, by the way? He would be the

fifth Duke of Norfolk if his father hadn't forfeited the title."

"Didn't you know that his mother's father had died and that he had inherited that title? He is called Earl of Arundel instead of the Earl of Surrey, and Anne is called Countess."

"What about Parliament?" Southwell demanded.

"Oh, Parliament decided to simplify martyrdom. There are two new statutes against Catholics. Sir Francis Walsingham's brain grew tired concocting plots and accusing Catholics of conspiring in such a way that they could be tried under the old statute as traitors. Now, if one wants to be a martyr, all one needs to do is to be a Catholic priest, born since Her Majesty came to the throne and living in her realm. Statute 27 Eliz.c.2 they call it, or the Act of 1585."

Southwell's face flushed. "Then I would qualify, were I sent to England."

"Perfectly. When I get old I shall be boasting of my cousin the martyr."

"Tony!" protested Southwell again, and then asked, "But can the Earl of Arundel be accused of being a traitor? We do not get all of the fine points of the English law here in Rome."

"So you question me as an authority," replied Copley, his expression quizzical. "Under the Statute 23 Eliz. c. 1, I imagine he could be said to have withdrawn his allegiance and adhered to the Queen's enemy, the Pope. And, whereas he gave Her Majesty jewels at New Year's previously, he made no gift last year because he was in restraint."

"You know he was the godson of King Philip of Spain," said Southwell.

"Yes. I think Walsingham will invent a plot for him readily enough. They say he discovers hundreds of plots in which the Queen of Scots is supposed to be involved. It is a shame. But he really believes that it would be better to have her killed privately than to have all the bother of a trial."

70

"Tony!" Southwell was deeply troubled by the assertion.

"Well, I thought that I would make you acquainted with affairs at home. By the way, I forgot to put a peg in my hole when I came out. Before Pope Gregory died, I could think of myself as a guest of the Pope, so to speak, a gentleman living on his bounty because my recusant parents were impoverished by fines paid for their allegiance to him. But now, with a new Pope, shall I run back and put a peg in my hole?"

"I remembered your peg," Southwell assured him. "I put it in and told the porter that you were with me. But Tony, why did you come to Rome if you are not more devout than I suspect?"

"To be a poet, Robert. There is poetry in our Shelley-Copley blood. Take you, for instance: you cannot deny that you like to make rhymes. And Italy is the place to learn to be a poet because of Dante and Petrarch and the rest. Sir Philip Sidney says—"

Southwell interrupted him, somewhat severely. "What would your mother think of your coming to Italy to learn to be not a priest but a poet?"

"And what would Pope Gregory have thought if he had known it when you induced him to give me an allowance? By the way, what about this new Pope, Sixtus V?"

"He is different from Pope Gregory. Very strict, I understand. And he has a great interest in architecture."

"And in poetry?" Copley was laughing.

"No. Not your kind," responded Southwell with a smile. "It is said that he will have the dome of Saint Peter's completed, and that, if he lives, there will be new buildings in Rome, and fine clear water brought from the hills again. *Aqua felice.*"

"*Aqua felice . . . aqua felice . . . aqua felice,*" repeated Copley. "What a lovely sound it has!"

"Words, always words. I know. I love the sound, too. Do

you see that live oak over yonder, close to the little amphitheater on the side of the hill? The poet Tasso has been in the habit of sitting under it."

"He who wrote *Jerusalem Delivered*?" demanded Copley with excitement. "Might he be there now? I must meet him!"

"He is insane. Locked up," answered Southwell wryly, glancing at his cousin.

"Like my poetic self. I do feel incarcerated at the English College, Robert."

Southwell rose, and drew Copley to his feet. "Come. There are worse prisons, as you know . . . with racks and dungeons . . . and. . . ."

"Oh, forget them," exclaimed Copley. "Let's race down the hill!"

"I have been ordained," Southwell reminded him.

"All the more reason to have fun while you can," said Copley. "Tuck up your cassock! One, two, three, go!"

Chapter 12

The market in the Campo dei Fiori was temporarily quiet. Large white parasols were open to protect the flowers and vegetables from the late morning heat, and the vendors were taking their repose in the shade. Southwell, walking toward the Chiesa Nuova from the English College, was reviewing the year that had passed since he and his cousin Anthony Copley had sat on the Janiculum Hill and discussed conditions in England. It had been a difficult year, for he had had to be kind and just in his relations with certain students who found the Jesuit rule at the College irksome, and who had developed a prejudice against the Sodality of the Blessed Virgin, a group devoted to works of charity among the poor. As Prefect of Studies and in charge of the Sodality, Southwell might have been the target for their thrusts, but he thanked God that he had avoided all personal quarrels and maintained the courtesy and serenity consistent with his calling.

For him, the struggle with College factions was at an end, for now, at last, his orders had come. He was to leave the following day, May 8, 1586, for England. Father Henry Garnet would go with him, and instead of walking, as other missioners had done, they would have horses for their journey. All of the final preparations were made, and he had provided for young Anthony.

Southwell had saved this noon hour for a call that he wanted to make alone. Like Sherwin, he could not leave Rome without the blessing of Father Philip Neri. From year to year his admiration for the simple, wise, loving priest had grown as he had watched Rome yielding to his influence. He knew that he and the other young Englishmen had been fortunate to be in the city when it was normal to be devout, to adore the Blessed Sacrament and to sing the praise of Mary . . . and he understood that the prevalent piety was largely due to Philip Neri.

Reaching the vast church that had been built by Father Philip and his companions, he paused a minute to pray, then took the long stair that led from the side door to the old priest's roof-top apartment. Quiet prevailed, and for a moment, seeing Father Philip's door ajar, he wondered if he had gone out. Then he observed that the door to the tiny chapel was open with a sign on it that read, "Silence! The Father is celebrating

Mass." He knew that Father Philip had the privilege of offering Mass privately in this roof-top chapel, and he had heard that he let his altar boy go off to dinner if he forgot and prayed too long. This had happened today, and Southwell slipped into the chapel unobserved by Father Philip, who stood at the altar adoring Our Lord in the consecrated Host. He was completely rapt in prayer.

Southwell knelt and prayed.

Presently there was a little stir. A dark-eyed lad came into the chapel, went up close to the altar, and Father Philip continued and finished his Mass.

Southwell knelt motionless until the venerable priest discovered him and approached. "Your final blessing, Father, please," he asked.

Father Philip made the Sign of the Cross, uttered the words of benediction in his silvery voice, then laid his hands on the young priest's head. "You are about to leave?" he asked.

"Tomorrow, the Feast of Saint Michael the Archangel."

"We shall never see each other again in this life, Roberto. But Heaven is ahead."

"Pray that I may be faithful," Southwell said.

"You will be. And I have a message for small Ralph Emerson, your lay brother who is in a London prison. Tell him that I remember him at Mass." Then, with characteristic tenderness, Father Philip bade Southwell farewell.

Father Robert Southwell and Father John Deckers, Jesuits, sat in the shade close to the Chapel at Douay. Deckers was watching Southwell's thin fingers as he veined a leaf, just as he had done in this very spot almost ten years before.

"You will rest with us here at Anchin College after your long horseback journey from Rome, Robert?"

"We cannot linger, John. We are known to Sir Francis

Walsingham's spies; there are many of them here in Douay, Englishmen, some of whom live in disguise in the English colony."

"But in our Jesuit College of Anchin, where I am teaching, you would be safe."

"No. I shall never be safe again on earth. Why do you wish to delay my going to England, you who but ten years ago were speeding me on the way to martyrdom?" Southwell smiled, glanced up at his companion, then continued the delicate veining of the leaf.

"I am not trying to hold you back, Robert," Deckers assured him. "But, since I succeeded in making a Jesuit of you, I want you to serve God a long time in the Society. According to news from England, Walsingham's men are alerted. Some say that Walsingham hopes to intercept messages that will prove that Catholic conspirators are plotting with the Queen of Scots. Some intimate that his secretary, Thomas Phelippes, an experienced forger, writes messages, dictated by Walsingham himself, and that presently he will produce papers seemingly written by conspirators and confiscated at some likely spot. You know, of course, that Walsingham is a fanatic and hates the Church. Lord Burghley hates the Church also, but he and Queen Elizabeth perhaps love England more than they abhor Rome. It is Walsingham's pursuivants whom you have to fear, and they are keen for arrests right now. It seems a waste to spend years in preparation for the Mission, and then to be captured and thrown into prison immediately on arrival."

"That is true," agreed Southwell, "but wasn't it you who reminded me ten years ago that Jesuits were soldiers, obedient to their commander? John, I have my orders from Father General. From here, I go to our college at St. Omer, and from there to Boulogne or some other port from which we are to cross secretly to England."

"That being so, you go, of course," agreed Deckers and quoted the Jesuit motto, "*Ad majorem Dei gloriam.*"

"Yes, 'for the greater glory of God,' I hope," responded Southwell. Then, producing from an inner pocket a slender wallet, he handed it to his friend with the request, "Take this. Use the contents for the English priests here who will go on the Mission. It is difficult to get funds through. You, being Flemish, will not be suspected of holding them."

"I gladly undertake the service. But you will write to me?"

"Yes. Twice. Once from St. Omer, and once from the port from which we sail for England. To write you from England might endanger others. But you will have news of me through our messengers who get word through to the Continent. Walsingham has his underground; we have ours, also."

"Ours works '*Ad majorem Dei gloriam.*' One cannot say the same for his," replied Deckers, carefully pocketing the wallet that he had been holding.

Southwell rose, and followed by Deckers, went into the chapel. There they knelt together as they had ten years before. Southwell offered himself in the words of Ignatius Loyola, "Receive, O Lord, my liberty." Deckers could not think what he should ask of God for his friend, so he bowed his head and prayed, "Thy will be done."

Some days later Southwell, having written from St. Omer as he had promised, reached the port of Boulogne from which he would set sail for England. He was excited but, as he had told his friend Deckers years before, he was articulate and found it natural to write. He sat down and penned a letter that is a record of true friendship, one of the famous letters of the English Martyrs.

"Being now exposed to utmost dangers, I address you, my Father, from the threshold of death, imploring the aid of your prayers that, as once you reawakened in me the breath of life when I was ready to die, so now by your prayers I may either escape the death of the body for further use, or endure it with courage."

Having thus thanked Deckers for his part in strengthening him in his Jesuit vocation, Southwell gave the letter to a messenger. He then joined Father Garnet and, in the twilight, went on board the boat that had been engaged to take them across the Channel by night, and land them on the English coast between Folkestone and Dover.

Chapter 13

Nobody observed a twenty-five-year-old gentleman who walked into the London prison known as the Counter-in-the-Poultry late one July evening in the year 1586. Even the door-keeper, into whose open palm he pressed a heavy coin, failed to remark his appearance, and could not have said that he was thin, of medium height, with auburn hair, and that he wore a black serge suit. Walsingham's pursuivants had a description of him and were on the lookout, but somehow Robert South-well, who had been in England about two weeks, seemed to go wherever he pleased and remain unnoticed.

He had landed July 7 with his traveling companion Father Henry Garnet and had ridden horseback to London, entering the city through Southwark, where he had Catholic friends in the Marshalsea Prison and the Clink, in Lord Montague's house and other dwellings. Southwark had been known to him since his youth, for here were some of Sir Thomas

Copley's holdings, including Rochester House and the Maze. But, on this return to England, every spot had taken on new meaning for him. The heads impaled on spikes on the Gatehouse of London Bridge might well be those of martyrs whom he had known and loved; the Tower of London, with its many leads and dungeons, seemed altogether different because it had witnessed the sufferings of his friends.

And now the London prisons, the Gatehouse, Bridewell, the Fleet, were his regular haunts; Marshalsea Prison, so old that nobody knew what its beginnings were, and formerly used for debtors and pirates, was full of his aristocratic recusant friends. There were sixty rooms there, and a regular arrangement by which prisoners came and went at will, paying, of course, for the privilege. He had celebrated Mass there, and preached about Mary Magdalen. Mass was forbidden, but the Catholics had contrived hiding places for altar vessels, missals and vestments, and there were certain prisoners' rooms ideally situated for services; there were even apertures through which Holy Communion could be distributed to persons kneeling in the room next to the one used for a chapel. During Mass hours, the well-bribed guards looked the other way or announced their rounds with heavy stamping so as not to surprise their benefactors.

In contrast, Bridewell was a terrible prison, with a treadmill and frightful practices. And the Fleet was very little better, although the warders at the Fleet were on the lookout for money, and prisoners could pay them for extra privacy or provisions. Newgate Prison, which had been renovated more than two centuries before with money left to the city by Dick Whittington, "Sir Richard Whittington, Lord Mayor of London," was in a shocking state, and was the place where those who supported a losing cause were imprisoned. They were all gruesome places for a young priest fresh from sunny Rome to visit at twilight.

Tonight's prison, the Counter-in-the-Poultry, was new to Southwell, and as he slipped from outside into the dank corridor, he wondered if he would find the friend whom he sought. Suddenly, out of the dusk, he heard a familiar voice.

"You have grown and filled out a bit. Come! Let's see if I can reach your shoulder."

"Brother Ralph!"

"Sh-h-h," warned tiny Ralph Emerson, who had accompanied Father Campion to England five years before. He put his finger to his lips. "Remember to play the stranger. There is nobody about now, but one never knows who is watching and will betray a visitor. You do well to wear black. Sometimes I think that Father Persons' bright garb attracted attention." He drew Southwell into an alcove and led him to a bench.

"I heard that you were here, and came at the first opportunity. Are you a prisoner because you were 'Mr. Patrick's' friend, or for what reason?"

"I loved Father Campion," replied Brother Ralph sadly. "But I was not a worthy friend. At his request I left him to do an errand, and he let himself get captured and hanged without me to care for him. I was arrested later, and am now almost hardened to prison life."

"Father Philip Neri knew that you were in prison, and told me to tell you that he remembered you at Mass," said Southwell.

"Blessed Father Philip. I believe he is a saint," answered the lay brother.

"But there is no serious charge against you?"

"I am in for what might be called 'Bible-running.' They captured me and held me here because I had been bringing books from beyond the seas. The Holy Bible that Dr. Gregory

Martin finished translating before he died . . . and many books of devotion."

Southwell looked at him lovingly. "Books as well as missioners are important to England. And easier to hide."

"That they are," agreed Brother Ralph. "But tell, what is the news of the great world outside? Any news of your family?"

"My mother died about the time my Uncle Thomas Copley did. I have not seen my father and brothers because I do not wish to embarrass them. My father goes to the Queen's services and is in favor at Court. My cousin George Cotton of Warblington has been in Fleet Prison. My sister Mary and my cousin Margaret Copley are fearless Catholics."

"Did Mary marry?"

"Yes. She married Edward Banister. His parents are devout recusants. They have come to London from Hampshire and are living at Southampton House."

"And Margaret Copley?"

"She is to marry a Gage."

"Not Robert Gage!" exclaimed Brother Ralph.

"No. His brother John."

"There is something afoot. We get all the rumors in prison. And Robert Gage is involved, I fear, just because he is bored. He is one of a crowd of daredevils playing into Walsingham's hands."

"It has to do with the Queen of Scots?" asked Southwell.

"So they say. The prison walls whisper it."

"Always, as long as I can recall, there have been plots, real or imagined, to put her on the throne. But have you any accurate information?"

"No. There is a restlessness among the young, they say."

"Robert Gage. And who else?" demanded Southwell.

"I do not know for sure. And remember that prison whispers are not always to be trusted. Is the name Anthony Babington familiar to you?"

"Yes, he was in the entourage of the Queen of Scots, as a page, and he went surety for John Gerard when he was paroled after he had been arrested on his return from France, and agreed to pay the fine if Gerard could escape to the Continent to study."

"Yes. And Gerard escaped. He was on his way to Rome when you came away. You must have passed each other. You met him at Douay years ago, of course. But, about Babington. Something is in the air. And I very much fear that he is too credulous not to be used by Sir Francis Walsingham. And there are others whom I do not trust: Gifford, who was at the English College with you, Tyrrell, and Poley. Beware of them." In the dim light, Brother Ralph reached out and touched Southwell's arm, and asked, "Have you been with Father Weston at all?"

"Yes. We spent a night with him at his little house. He had a visit from Babington shortly after our arrival. He received him privately, and then came to Father Garnet and me and said that he thought we would all benefit by a stay in the country. He did not say why."

"And where did you go to refresh yourselves?"

Southwell responded by singing in a low voice Sir Edward Dyer's line, "My mind to me a kingdom is," that William Byrd had set to music.

"Ah, I know! You were somewhere with the Queen's Chapel Master. He is a loyal Catholic and can be trusted to the ends of the earth. He writes music for Masses and composes madrigals and goes his way almost unmolested. Byrd is a wonder."

There was a heavy step close by, and Brother Ralph rose, saying in a loud voice, "No. There is no need to try to get money from me, sir. I am without resources. And I suggest that it is late." Then, when the guard had passed, Brother Ralph knelt on the pavement and whispered, "Your blessing, Father Robert. And pray for me at Mass. If only I were in the Marshalsea or the Clink, I could hear Mass."

Robert blessed the Jesuit Brother, laying his hands affectionately on his head. And then, walking rapidly, he left the prison. What were Gifford and his crowd up to, he wondered, and how was Walsingham influencing over-trustful Babington? He must warn Father Weston and Father Garnet that there was mischief abroad.

Chapter 14

Southwell walked up and down in the late autumn sunshine. He kept close to the garden wall that protected his path from view. Now and then he raised his eyes from his breviary and noticed the fruit trees trained against the wall and the trim grass plot in which stood a sun dial. He did not wear a cassock, but was dressed, as was his custom, in a black serge suit. He had been in England almost six months, and he felt that he had done well to follow Brother Ralph's advice and dress inconspicuously; like Sir Richard Shelley, he believed that priests who were dressed as men of fashion were spotted because they still behaved as priests, not quarreling or using coarse language.

Presently he closed his breviary, slipped it into his pocket, and began to pace the path more rapidly, his hands behind his back. This was a sheltered spot, a walled garden close beside Lord Vaux's house at Hackney, near London. He had been living here for several months.

Lord Vaux and his family were Southwell's cousins, as people reckoned kinship in the 16th Century. They were staunch Catholics. The family consisted of Lord and Lady Vaux, their son Harry, a young man who served the priests as George Gilbert had, and who hoped to be a Jesuit some day, and Harry's sisters Anne and Eleanor. Eleanor was the widow of Edward Brooksby, whose brother William had been in Paris and Rome with Southwell; she had adopted a little cousin, Frances Burrows, whose mother had died. Southwell had not yet seen eleven-year-old Frances or Mrs. Brooksby, for they had been at Harrowden, one of Lord Vaux's country places, ever since he had been living at Hackney. But he had met their connection, Sir Thomas Tresham, a strict and fearlessly outspoken Catholic, and he had become very devoted to Harry Vaux, who frequently rode into the city with him on horseback in the morning, and escorted him back at dusk.

Since the house had a chapel, or Mass-chamber, reached by a narrow, steep stair, and a hiding place for visiting priests, it was an ideal arrangement for Southwell to live there and to go back and forth to London to visit the Catholics who were in prison.

Now, as he walked up and down, he thought of how much had happened since July. Brother Ralph had been right when he suspected that trouble was brewing. Sir Francis Walsingham had used Gifford, who had once been a student at Douay and Rome, Robert Poley and others, to bring to light a plot that was called the Babington Plot. Southwell was sure that Walsingham schemed much of it, that documents had been falsified, and that Babington's youth and simplicity had been exploited to the full. Whatever the truth of it all, letters that passed between Babington and Mary, Queen of Scots, had been confiscated. Babington and some of his friends had been arrested in the woods near Harrow-on-the-Hill when they had sent to Uxendon, the Bellamy house, asking for food. One of the Bellamy boys and Robert Gage and others had been horribly executed along with Babington himself, and the poor Queen of Scots was a closer prisoner than ever. She had been convicted of conspiring against the Queen, and was now awaiting her Cousin Elizabeth's order for her beheading.

Southwell sighed when he thought of the enmity between the two Queens, and of the suffering that it had caused among Catholics. There had been a general search for all Catholics. Good Father William Weston had been arrested and made prisoner. Southwell's Aunt Katherine Copley, Anthony's mother, and her kinsman Father Nicholas Smith, had been arrested at Gatton, the Copleys' house in Surrey, and were now in Fleet Prison. Margaret Copley and John Gage had also been imprisoned, but had been freed, and had since married.

Southwell's sister Mary, Edward Banister's wife, was the only member of his immediate family whom he had seen since his arrival in London. Blue-eyed Mary had a way with her, and she managed to visit the Marshalsea and Fleet prisons as readily as Southwell himself did. He believed that she could persuade even the Tower of London guards to admit her if she so desired.

Thinking of Mary, he smiled. Then his expression saddened. He had returned to England with the hope of helping all Catholics, and the very ones he wanted the most to help, his father and his brothers, he had not even seen. His father was well known at Court and, as his uncle had assured him, there were many of his Southwell kin in high places, including Sir Robert Southwell, who had married the Lord Admiral's daughter.

Southwell glanced toward the sun dial and then looked up. The sun was low, but the garden wall still gave off some warmth. Swallows were circling overhead and pigeons cooing, and he thanked God for the peace.

Suddenly, as if a whirlwind had hit the garden, a young girl with two dogs on leashes burst through a gate in the wall, and threw herself at Southwell's feet. She knelt, unfastening the dogs, and exclaiming, "Down, Gub! Quick, your blessing, Father! Down, Mars! Down! Quick, Father, bless me! The pursuivants might be watching, so I couldn't kneel without the dogs. I suppose you know that I am Frances."

Southwell, smiling, made the Sign of the Cross.

Frances rose, the leash in her hand, and Gub and Mars rushed into the flower beds to chase a rabbit.

"You are Mrs. Brooksby's Frances?" asked the priest.

"Yes, Father. Frances Burrows. She adopted me when my mother died, when I was just five years old and my father sent me with my nurse to the Queen's services. Don't be alarmed; I never conformed. I invariably went to sleep instead of listening to those long Protestant sermons, and as I always fell off the bench and woke up crying, Nannie had to take me out to play in the churchyard with the tombstones. You see, I was made a Catholic by the Protestant sermons. I was never a Protestant and you do not have to reconcile me."

"No, that is evident," said Southwell.

"Here, Gub! Here, Mars! Stop digging," shouted Frances. "He is named Mars because he is a fighter," explained Frances. "And Gub is named for Saint Francis of Assisi."

"Because he is gentle?" asked Southwell.

"No. He isn't. 'Gub' is short for Gubbio, the Italian town where St. Francis tamed the wolf."

How it all brought back sunny Italy and the lovely country-side of Umbria! The priest looked at the young girl in her gage green gown with starched lace ruff, stiff skirt, and tight bodice, her curly hair and vivid pink cheeks, and from her to the cir-cling swallows and the dogs that lay obediently at her feet. His reverie was interrupted by her demand, "Do you think that I will be a saint?"

"You have the opportunity. Shall we walk up and down so that you will not catch cold?"

"Yes, I am overheated. We have just arrived from Harrowden and I had to take the dogs for a run. But, about my being a saint."

"Yes, tell me about that," he agreed, as they fell into step and began to pace the path.

"It happened at Harrowden. One evening a very tired Man, dressed in white, came to me when I was on the lawn near the house, and told me that He was hungry. I told Him to go stand outside the pantry window, and that I would get food in the kitchen and pass it out to Him. Cook was furious, for I begged the best of everything from her, and I am not supposed to eat between meals. Then I took it to the Stranger. He smiled and thanked me. He had beautiful, gentle eyes. He went away: Nobody else saw Him. He did not pass through the village . . . and. . . ?"

"Yes. I know what you wonder," said Southwell. "Certainly God wants you to be a saint. You are a brave Catholic. And you have a kind heart."

"Well," she replied, looking up into his face, "I am a little like Mars and Gub. I know how to fight. I must take them to the kennels now, and then I shall have my supper in the nursery. I am eleven, but some gentlemen have arrived. You know the kind of gentlemen I mean." She stood on tiptoe and whispered, "Priests in disguise," and then continued aloud, "Grandfather and Uncle Harry are going to entertain them at supper. And, by the way, Grandfather sent me to tell you that they awaited you in the drawing room." Again she stood on tiptoe, "We shall have three Masses in the chapel before daylight tomorrow. And I have to go to confession first." She sped away as boisterously as she had arrived, and the dogs, still unleashed, bounded along beside her.

That evening, Lord Vaux, his son Harry, and their in-law

Sir Thomas Tresham, the two newly arrived priests and South-well discussed conditions in England. All were concerned because the spies were active everywhere, and the London Magistrate, Richard Young, was sending search parties into Catholic houses. The house which Southwell had visited with Father Weston and Father Garnet when he first returned to England had been searched, and the owner sent to prison. The houses of the musician William Byrd and the nobleman Francis Browne had been searched, also. Gatton, Warblington and Roughey, country houses that belonged to Southwell's family, were known to the spies and were dangerous places for priests to visit. It was necessary to know which dwellings were safe, which had hidden chapels and hiding holes for the clergy, for Catholics were determined to continue to go to confession, hear Mass, and go to Holy Communion, no matter what the danger. And the priests were there to spend their lives helping them, blessing marriages, baptizing babies and anointing the sick.

Lord Vaux said, "I fear that our houses are constantly watched, both this house and Harrowden. My daughters suggest that they rent conveniently located places in the country where hiding holes can be prepared: a house such as Baddesley Clinton, for instance, where there is a moat, with a drain that could be diverted, its channel used for a secret entrance. Our hiding place here is an excellent one, I think, and as it is close to the chapel, which is immediately over the front portico, and reached only by means of a narrow stair, there would be some chance of escape should the searchers come. But we are so close to London that the peril of capture is very great. Father Southwell is already familiar with the house, but I shall show you gentlemen our arrangements before you retire."

Lord Vaux and the priests rose, and Southwell bade them good night and went to his room to get two letters that Harry Vaux was to dispatch for him secretly the next day.

Very early the following morning, long before the November sun had risen, Southwell went to the chapel, heard the confessions of the family and servants, and said Mass. Just as he had finished his Mass, and before another had begun, there was a sound of pounding at the front door, followed by shouts, tramping, demands for entrance. There could be only one reason for such disturbance. The armed searchers had come.

Lady Vaux and Southwell collected the sacred vessels and missal and put them in a concealed chest. The family and servants rose to their feet. Frances, who had been kneeling near the door, opened it and went quick as lightning down the narrow stairs. Mrs. Brooksby, alarmed for the girl's safety with the ruffians below, followed as fast as she could and, midway on the stairs, paused. She saw Frances standing in the front hall confronting the men who had broken in, their weapons drawn, ready to lash about in all directions.

"Stop, immediately," commanded Frances. "Put up your swords, or else my mother will die at the sight of them!"

Mrs. Brooksby, on the narrow stair, truly looked pale and weak enough to die of fright, and the men hesitated. They knew that Mass must have been in progress, for the ladies were up and dressed at that early hour, but they could scarcely pass Mrs. Brooksby on the stairs. One of the searchers seized Frances' arm and held his dagger at her breast. He told her that if she did not disclose the whereabouts of the priests, he would stab her in the heart.

She retorted, "Do so, if you dare! It will be the hottest blood you ever shed!"

Fortunately Lord Vaux, who with his son had seen the priests safely into the hiding place, appeared and demanded a warrant if the men were to search the house. The delay effected by Frances and by Lord Vaux's demand for a warrant was successful, and the priests were not captured, although the pursuivants banged furniture, broke woodwork, and were sometimes so close to the cramped refuge that it seemed as if their swords would slash through the partition.

Harry Vaux was arrested, with Southwell's letters in his possession. His clerk was also taken to prison.

Southwell had to remain in hiding for several days, for the searchers surrounded the house and made various raids. But finally, they knew that their quest was hopeless for the time being, and withdrew. Southwell realized that his presence was a danger to the family, for the letters found on Harry gave away the fact that he was staying there. He would have gone to prison himself, could he have freed Harry, but Sir Thomas Tresham assured him that the young man was experienced and would get himself out. He did not succeed in this immediately, however, and when Southwell slipped away to the south of England to his Catholic cousins, he was very unhappy to think that two brave men, Harry Vaux and his clerk, were in jail while he was still free. But he knew that the laity needed priests and, although he had always wanted to be a martyr, he was willing to suffer a long time serving his fellow Catholics before he gave his life for his Faith.

Chapter 15

A fog was shrouding the Thames when late one December afternoon a slim gentleman dressed in black hurried out of Lord Montague's house, which was at the Southwark end of

London Bridge. He looked up at the martyrs' heads impaled on spikes on the Gatehouse, and breathed a prayer for courage. Then he mingled with the crowd on the bridge. Shops lined the old structure, but in the gathering gloom nobody paused to buy. Thanks to the fact that the evening was too dark and wet for even the bravest to be ferried across the Thames, practically all London-bound traffic crammed the bridge.

The pedestrian, who had visited Catholics in the Clink Prison and the Marshalsea before calling on his friend Francis Browne at Lord Montague's, was wondering where he would spend the night. His cousin George Cotton of Warblington, John Cotton's father, had a house in Fleet Street close to Fleet Prison, where Lady Katherine Copley was confined because she had sheltered a priest at Gatton and practiced her religion. He knew that he could stay at Cotton's house but, should he be caught there, his cousin, who had already spent years in prison, might be arrested again. Perhaps it would be wiser to go to an inn in Holborn where he had left a change of clothes. He decided to put off a decision concerning the night until he had stopped at Fleet Prison for a visit to his Aunt Katherine.

With an uneasy feeling that he was being followed across the bridge, he quickened his pace without looking behind him. He remembered that Lord Montague's house, frequented by Catholics, was known to the pursuivants. Perhaps a searcher, commissioned by Young, had followed him from there. Presently he felt himself jostled, and glancing to his left, saw that a middle-aged woman, wrapped in a heavy black shawl, had fallen into step with him. He did not speak, nor did the woman, until they reached the London end of the bridge.

As he turned, she turned with him and asked in a low tone, "Father Southwell?"

It was growing dark, but he could see enough of her face

to know that it was unfamiliar. "You are seeking some one?" he asked, without saying who he was.

"I followed you from Lord Montague's house. I am not a Catholic and you have never seen me. But I am a messenger from one whose husband's family and yours have been allied for many years."

Southwell listened carefully. The woman's accent was that of the Northern counties. "My family is large . . . spread through many districts of the realm," he said evasively.

"With many members at Court," continued the woman, walking sturdily beside him. "But I refer to your close kin in Norfolk and Sussex. I come from the Countess Anne to request your presence at Arundel House in the Strand."

Southwell gasped. Could he believe his ears? Was this avowed non-Catholic an impostor sent to trick him into endangering Philip Howard's wife? Philip was a prisoner in the Tower. Anne and her two children, the youngest of whom Philip had never seen, had quarters in Arundel House, which belonged to them but which had been seized by the Crown because they were Catholics. Was there some plan to trap the Howards through him, a Catholic priest?

The woman must have known that he was puzzled, for she began to explain in a low voice, "I am her ladyship's serving woman, having been with her father's family, the Dacres, for many years. The Countess said that you would be glad to help her when you heard that Father Martin Aray was in prison. He used to say Mass at Arundel House before he was captured."

"It is your belief that the Countess Anne wishes to have a chaplain?" asked Southwell.

"A known person. A family friend. After all, she is by rights the Duchess of Norfolk, the First Lady of the Realm, and would be treated as such if she and the Earl would give up their religion. It is said, you know, that he could regain the title forfeited by his father, if he would be sensible and be a Protestant. Well, a Duchess cannot leave her babies and slip away secretly to hear Mass, can she, even a Papist Duchess who is only called Countess?"

Southwell smiled to himself. Here was an old family retainer who believed in the rights of the nobility. No doubt she knew, as he did, that Anne Howard had slipped out by night years before and had been reconciled by a priest to the Catholic religion, and that this had happened even before her husband's conversion after Campion's trial. He no longer thought it remotely possible that this ungainly woman was a spy for the Government. He walked along thinking, his companion trudging steadily beside him. They had turned in the direction of the Fleet and the Strand and as Arundel House, set in its several acres, faced out on the Thames, they were walking toward it.

Southwell reviewed in his mind the long family association, including his grandfather's betrayal of Philip Howard's ancestor, the Earl of Surrey. Perhaps he, as a priest, could do something to atone for that. Four years Philip's junior, he had never seen him, although he had been tempted to try to get a glimpse of him in the distance pacing the leads at the Tower of London. He knew that Philip Howard, after he had been reconciled to the Church, had decided to leave England and live abroad, and that he had written a letter to Queen Elizabeth explaining his doing so. He had left the letter with his sister to be delivered to Her Majesty after his departure. But he had been captured in the Channel, taken to London and imprisoned in the Tower.

More than a year had passed since that, and although Lord Burghley had been his guardian, and although the Queen had accepted jewels from him in former years at Court, he had been rigorously treated. Not once had he seen the Countess or his small daughter since he had been in the Tower. Southwell knew that Philip, who knew little about the Catholic religion, was making a great sacrifice for his Faith. But he was not yet condemned to die for it. Southwell pondered the matter and his own course.

"You are thinking that Arundel House is a dangerous place because close to Somerset House, where Her Majesty stays so often," said the woman, breaking in on his thoughts. "That is true. And you are a marked man, Father Southwell; descriptions of you are abroad. But we could shelter you at Arundel House. You would have a hidden apartment, and you could go out at dusk to visit your friends in the prisons. The old nursery might do for you. And there is a garden. Also, there are landing stairs to the river, and a Catholic boatman might be engaged to meet you there when you had errands. Perhaps it would be wiser, however, for you to go out when the laborers quit work for the day. I could prepare a smock for you, an entirely clean black smock, and nobody would know you were not a carpenter. That is, if you wore a hat, otherwise your red hair. . . ."

Southwell chuckled. "You have undoubtedly seen me in the daylight," he said.

"Yes, Father. The truth is that the Countess, wishing to have the Sacraments of her Church, ordered me to make inquiry. . . . I have been watching you for some time, and I decided. . . ."

Southwell chuckled again. "Sir Francis Walsingham would find you a great asset in his spy system."

"Never!" exclaimed the woman. "I'll have nothing to do with Sir Francis! Do you know that we, the Countess and I, were virtually imprisoned in the house of Sir Thomas Shirley when our Tommy was born, after the Earl's arrest? My lady had to write Sir Francis and beg him to let us live in one of our own houses, hers or the Earl's, I mean. We have many houses besides Arundel Castle and Arundel House, you know. No Sir Francis Walsingham or Lord Burghley for me! Secretaries of the Queen, they call themselves, but I call them—"

"Sh-h-h, be careful," he cautioned.

"Well, you can scarcely see your hand before your face in this thickening fog, and nobody is near to hear me," she retorted. "Goodness knows where you would be by now without me!"

"Have we passed the alley to Fleet Prison?" he asked, for he had half a mind to quit her there and call on his Aunt Katherine.

"Long since, Father. We are almost at the gates of Arundel House. The Countess awaits you. The porter knows me, of course, and you are a gentleman just arrived from the North. You are calling on the Countess with news of the estates of my Lord Dacres, her brother." Saying which, with a gentle elbow nudge, she piloted him through the wicket, past the porter, and into the courtyard.

"We have the use of only seven rooms, some lobbies and a garden, for which we have to pay rent to the Crown, although it is our house. All because of being Catholics," muttered the guide as she directed their steps to an entry. "Her Ladyship said to bring you to the nursery, it being her hour to be there with the little girl and the new baby. The children are already baptized Papists, so you do not need to go back for any of your fonts and pitchers and things. She wants to talk to you."

He followed her into the house and through dimly lighted apartments, some of which were carpeted, others strewn with rushes from which came a pleasant fragrance of lavender and thyme. Finally reaching a closed door, the woman rapped gently four times and, admission being granted in a soft voice, she led him into a warm room. The draperies were drawn. There was no light save that from a log fire in the chimney.

94

Before the fire sat a lady with an infant in her arms and a small girl snuggled against her.

"Father Southwell is here, your ladyship," said the serving woman.

The Countess Anne dropped to her knees, holding the baby in her left arm, and caressing the little girl with her right. "Bless us, Father," she murmured, raising her hand to make the Sign of the Cross. He blessed her and the children, begging God's aid for them. As the serving woman forestalled his effort to help Anne Howard to rise, he noticed how tall she was in her plain gown, and how fair and thin. She was in her thirtieth year, and a calm grace accompanied her delicate beauty. In her way, she was as self-confident as her serving woman had been. And he found himself thinking that she had perfect confidence in him, also.

"So Melissa found you, Father. I was not expecting your call this evening, but I am happy to see you. Will you sit here by the fire with the children and me for a while? It would not be wise to send to the kitchen, for I suspect that we have a spy in the scullery, but Melissa will bring you a nursery supper."

The woman withdrew noiselessly, as he answered, "The first nursery supper that I have had in many years. And I am grateful to you for thinking of it. I am cold and hungry and—"

"And captured by a Protestant pursuivant," she interrupted, smiling. "Father Aray, who celebrated Mass secretly here for the Catholics of our household, is in prison. Would it be prudent for you to come?"

"Prudent?" He smiled.

"Yes. I would not have you risk your life."

"I do not fear for my life. But I must not endanger you or your children. It was when I was living at Lord Vaux's house that Harry and his clerk William Harris were captured. Harry is still in Fleet Prison, and Harris, alas, in Bridewell. Since their arrest, I have moved from place to place lest I bring trouble on a Catholic family. . . . I have just returned to London, and shall not go out in the daylight as yet."

She seemed somewhat puzzled. "But we have Mass before dawn, and a very private Mass-chamber," she assured him.

"And has the priest's room access to a hiding place so that I would not be discovered and cause you trouble?" he demanded gravely. "It is wise to have an exit by which the priest can escape from the hiding place to the street so that the family can truthfully say that he is not in the house when the searchers come. But doubtless you have thought of that."

A log broke just then, and a brilliant light played on the Countess' face, showing her bewildered expression. But Southwell did not notice it, for he was looking at the serving woman, who had entered silently and was lighting candles and placing a tray in front of him.

"Pardon me, my lady. The old nursery lends itself perfectly. And there is a builder, doubtless known to the Father, one Nicholas Owen, who is very skilled in such matters."

Southwell almost jumped out of his chair. Nicholas Owen was a Jesuit lay brother, nicknamed "Little John." He was regularly employed by the Jesuits to construct secret rooms in recusants' houses. And here was a Protestant serving woman recommending him to the Countess of Arundel!

"Take the broth while it is hot," Melissa pursued with the freedom of an old servant. "And eat the egg, for it will give you strength. The bread is stale, I fear, but I didn't dare risk that spy in the pantry." She stood still until the priest had said grace, unfolded his napkin and topped the egg neatly, then she took the infant and the little girl from the Countess. As she started off to put the children to bed, she volunteered, "As for service, my lady, nobody would be more discreet than myself. He would be no trouble. Neat as a pin, I know, for I watched him break his egg. When your Ladyship wants me to show him his quarters, please tap for me."

Melissa moved off, and when she had left the room, Anne and Southwell laughed.

"Just like my old nurse," he said. "I was stolen by the gypsies when I was a baby and she went to the camp and found me. It was she who taught me to break an egg with dispatch."

"Your home was in Norfolk, wasn't it?"

"Yes. Near Norwich. Your husband's grandfather had a place in the neighborhood. How is the Earl?"

"Never really well since he has been in the Tower. If he were in the Marshalsea or the Fleet, we could see him. But only his estate agents and his valet are admitted to the Tower, and it is difficult to send private letters in with his business papers; but sometimes, we manage." She studied Southwell's face a second, then confided, "You know that Philip and I were brought up together. We were actually step-brother and sister. Ours was an arranged marriage. He was very gay, and had he been of a different family, the Queen would have made a favorite of him, I think. Perhaps he did not love me very much for a while. But he did his duty by the Realm; he always went faithfully to the meetings of Parliament. And. . . ." she hesitated a moment. "Well, after he saw Father Campion tried and condemned, he was reconciled to the Church by Father Weston. Then, when I told him that I had been reconciled secretly to our childhood religion, we began to love and understand each other. I was to have joined him in France, had he succeeded in getting there. I could not flee with a brand new baby. It is not Her Majesty's will that he see me or the children. And my Lord Burghley, who was our guardian after Philip's father was beheaded, seems to fear to annoy the Queen."

Southwell, eating the egg and nibbling the stale bread,

listened carefully. Could he fail to help this piteous lady? he asked himself.

"But, Father, finish your supper. And you have not said that you would agree to say Mass here."

"I agree very gladly. But will you promise me that you will not use your influence in my behalf should I be captured?"

"Prevent your receiving a martyr's crown?" she asked, smiling as she wiped tears from her eyes. "Father, I readily promise, for I have no influence. I am more helpless where the Queen is concerned than the lowliest woman in the land."

There were four soft raps on the door. "Come in," said Anne.

Melissa entered. "I thought that the fire might be low," she explained, "and that if Father Southwell had finished his supper, the hour was convenient. It is time for the guard to change."

Southwell and the Countess bade each other good night, and he followed Melissa away from the nursery.

He did not know until the Countess told him many months later that she had not expected him to live at Arundel House, merely to go there occasionally to hear confessions and say Mass. The whole scheme was of Melissa's contriving.

"I am no Papist," the serving woman had confided to her mistress, after the interview in the nursery. "But Father Southwell is a blessed man, even if mistaken, and so young, with his boy's face and red hair, that I wanted to mother him. Then, too, we'd settle a score with my Lord Burghley and that fox-faced Sir Francis Walsingham by giving your Ladyship the consolations of your religion."

Chapter 16

Arundel House was so vast that it was possible to arrange a room with a private entrance without calling "Little John" from his work in country houses.

Southwell lived there quietly. He said Mass and heard confessions and was the chaplain for the Countess. His food was taken to him by Protestant Melissa, who kept watch for his safety. He left the mansion now and then, slipping out before dawn to say Mass in nearby Fleet Prison, or at dusk to go to Newgate or the Counter, but all day long he was alone. Then he knew how good God had been to let him like to read and write.

He read his breviary, Saint Bernard's Sermons and some of the books that had been smuggled in. And he wrote sermons, letters and poems.

When Philip Howard learned that there was a chaplain at Arundel House, he began to write asking spiritual direction; because he had not had Catholic instruction since he was a very small boy, many questions puzzled him. He sent letters to Southwell asking counsel, and Southwell replied, encouraging him to holy patience and heroism. When the Countess could not contrive other means to forward the correspondence, she sent it in the Earl's linen, carried by an old laundress who had access to the Tower.

At the Countess' request, Southwell wrote a book entitled *A Short Rule for a Good Life*. The Catholics had not been to

Catholic schools or had priests to teach them for a long time, and they begged for written instruction. What was composed for one person was copied and circulated for many. For a book to be published, there had to be a license from the Stationers' Company, and, of course, a priest in hiding could not ask for a license, nor would one have been granted for a Catholic book.

Southwell had long had the habit of writing verses about the meditations that he made. Now, during his hidden life in Arundel House, the Hidden Life of Our Lord was much in his thoughts. He wrote many poems about Our Lady and Saint Joseph and the Child Jesus. Having asserted that "God lent His Paradise to Joseph's care," he told in verse how Our Lady and Saint Joseph were espoused, and about the Angel Gabriel's announcing to Mary the coming of the Infant Jesus, and he treated of the other mysteries of Christ's Childhood, the Nativity, the Presentation, the Flight into Egypt. Presently there were enough poems to make a small book called *Maeoniae*.

When dour Melissa would enter with a tray, she would set down the simple fare with an apology. There might be boiled mutton with dry prunes, and salad with an oil and vinegar dressing, or occasionally roasted meat.

One Friday, the serving woman brought nothing but bread and milk.

"It is the best I could do, Father. The spy in the pantry was watching. But, I could get some cold meats if. . . ."

"It is Friday, Melissa, the day Our Lord died," said Southwell, looking up from his writing. "Listen. I was making a verse just then about Our Lady's words to Jesus when He was crucified:

> What mist hath dimmed that glorious Face?
> What seas of grief my Son so toss?
> That golden rays of heavenly grace
> Are now eclipsed on the Cross.
>
> Jesu, my Son, my life and God. . . ."

The sound of a sob interrupted Southwell's reading, and Melissa, setting down the tray, said, "Here. Eat this. You shall not make a Catholic of me." She put her hand into her apron pocket, drew out a bag and emptied its contents on a plate. "Here are some nuts and raisins for you. I suppose even a Papist could eat those on a Friday."

Southwell exclaimed, "What a treat! I much prefer almonds to fish! Does that prove me a good Catholic?"

She grumbled something and left him.

When he had finished his meal to the very last raisin, and said grace, he took a new sheet of paper and began a letter to Father Aquaviva, Father General of the Jesuits. He dated it carefully, December 21, 1586. He told what difficulties Catholics had had since the Babington Plot, then continued, "About Parliament I say nothing, as I desire my letters, like my soul, to have absolutely nothing to do with matters of State." And he went on to describe the recusants' devotion to the Holy Eucharist: "The one remaining solace of the Catholics amidst all this trouble and turmoil is to refresh themselves with the Bread of Heaven."

Then, when he had finished that letter, because it was close to Christmas, he wrote to Father Agazzari. Wherever one might be, he thought, Christmas was the birthday of the Baby Jesus. Lines had been running in his head:

As I in hoary winter's night stood shivering in the snow,
Surprised I was with sudden heat which made my heart to glow;
And lifting up a fearful eye to view what fire was near,
A pretty Babe all burning bright did in the air appear.
And then he remembered the first lines of another verse that he had written about the Baby Jesus:

Let folly praise that fancy loves, I praise and love that Child
Whose heart no thought, whose tongue no word, whose hand
no deed defiled.

All through the Christmas season, it was Southwell's joy to give Holy Communion to his Catholic friends. Since Harry Vaux was in prison, it was fortunate that the Fleet had been chosen for him, for, years before when his father was imprisoned there, the family had found a way to have Mass in his room.

The winter wore on. Dawn came late and twilight early. As the Fleet was not far from Arundel House, Southwell could visit Harry Vaux and Lady Katherine Copley. One evening in February, when the workmen were leaving, Southwell slipped out in their company and made his way to the Fleet to call on Lady Katherine. The guards looked in the other direction as he entered and walked down a dark, damp corridor to his aunt's room. He knocked, then went around an improvised screen which gave a little privacy, and discovered the lady lying on a pallet in the corner. The stump of one candle was burning beside her, and by its light he could see her fingers moving mechanically.

"Aunt Katherine!"

"Why, Robert! I was saying my rosary on my fingers. They took my beads away from me when they brought me to jail." She started to rise.

"Lie still," he said, seating himself on a stool beside her.

"You have news of Anthony?" she asked.

"Father Rector writes that he is well," he replied.

"Oh, the blessed Roman sunshine!" she exclaimed. "How thankful I am to you for getting the Pope to shelter him there. Anthony is not steady like my Margaret and your sister Mary."

"Any news of my father and Tom?" he questioned. "It seems strange to be in London and never have a glimpse of either."

"I have not seen them, of course. Tom is forever in trouble, either in debt or in love with a girl at Court. And Her Majesty does not approve of love-making even when she is in a good

102

humor, and this winter, with the thought of the Queen of Scots to trouble her, she—"

The conversation was interrupted by a light tap, and around the screen came a tiny, bent, shawl-wrapped figure.

"Me leddy," began the intruder with a pronounced cockney accent, then, seeing the visitor, she straightened up, rushed across the room, knelt beside him and flung her arms around him. "Oh, Robert! My Robin! I had not dared hope that you would be here with Aunt Katherine. Is it safe for you to be here? I know that Sir Francis Walsingham's men have a description of you and are watching every jail."

"So this is who the old woman is," he said, lifting the candle and studying his sister Mary's face. She pushed back the black wool shawl from her brow and he looked at the auburn curls and the deep blue eyes.

"Robert, you are in danger. I think that I was followed, so I must leave before you do. I came to tell Aunt Katherine that the courier came through from Fotheringay to say that. . . ."

"That the Queen of Scots is dead?" demanded Lady Katherine. "God rest her soul. She was not always good, and she should not have yielded to Bothwell. But she had a hard life, and many temptations, and lately—"

Mary interrupted, "The Scottish Queen conducted herself with great dignity. To the end, she declared herself a true Catholic. She was beheaded on the eighth of February at Fotheringay, her faithful people around her, even her little dog. . . ." Mary hesitated and shuddered. "Her little dog was close to her. Nobody saw him until he ran out from beside her severed head, all covered with her blood. They say that Queen Elizabeth claims that she was trapped into giving the order for her execution." Mary began to sob.

"Mary, Mary," said Southwell gently, restoring the candle to its place, and laying his hand on his sister's shoulder. "God gave the Queen of Scots grace to die in the Faith. Pray now for our Queen, her cousin, that God make her merciful."

The candle spluttered, and the screen cast a weird, wavering shadow on the prison wall.

"Go, children. Go, while you have light enough to get out of the room," urged Lady Katherine. "Mary, your husband awaits you? Then, you leave first. Robert, hear my confession. Then you must leave, too."

A few moments later, as Southwell went cautiously through the ill-lit passages to the Strand, he was surprised to find that he was making a verse. "Words, words, words," he scolded himself. Nevertheless, he continued to string the phrases together:

> Alive a Queen, now dead I am a Saint;
> Once Mary called, my name now Martyr is;
> From earthly reign debarred by restraint,
> In lieu whereof I reign in heavenly bliss.
>
> Rue not my death, rejoice at my repose;
> It was no death to me but to my woe;
> The bud was opened to let out the rose,
> The chain was loosed to let the captive go.

Chapter 17

Queen Elizabeth's thoughts were diverted from the execution of the Queen of Scots by news of the raid that Sir Francis Drake made in the harbor of Cadiz. He destroyed many ships that King Philip was having built for an attack on England. The recusants did not want Spain to conquer England, but, because King Philip was a Catholic, the Government claimed that they did. It was a hard year for the Jesuits and their friends.

Father William Weston, the former Superior, being a prisoner, Father Henry Garnet, ten years Southwell's senior, became Superior of the Jesuits in England. Middle-aged, learned, musical, he seemed an easy-going person, never making a fuss over things. One reason for this was that he was a mathematician and very methodical. He gave his attention to organizing the missioners' lives. Because it was important for them to keep close to the thought of their vocation, he planned two annual meetings, one at Easter time and one in the fall, when they could make General Confessions and renew their vows. He also decided that certain priests would work in London, others in the country, and that there must be special houses, with hiding places prepared by Brother Nicholas Owen, for the priests' use.

The Countess of Arundel gave him help. Since she did not like to be at Arundel House when the Queen stayed in the neighborhood at Somerset House, she had found two suburban dwellings, one in Acton and another near Bishopsgate. These were familiar to Southwell and Father Garnet, who wanted to set up a printing press, and the Countess consented to their use.

Six or seven years had passed since the exciting days when Father Edmund Campion's *Rationes Decem* was printed at Stonor Park, watched over by George Gilbert. The pursuivants had followed the Catholics there and seized the press; perhaps the gaily dressed company had roused their suspicions. This must not happen again, and Southwell, who knew how to move without attracting attention, managed to get his press set up and books printed on it so secretly that to this day there is no record of its exact location, although there are rare copies of its output.

Southwell had been writing for the recusants' instruction and his works had been copied by hand, but now they were to have a wider circulation. It is not hard to imagine how excited he was when he held his first printed book in his hands and realized that the English prose scribbling, that he had thought of as a temptation, had prepared him to write a book that would spread the knowledge of a holy life. Entitled *An Epistle of Comfort, To The Reverend Priestes & To The Honorable, Worshipful & other of the Laye sort restrayned in Durance for the Catholicke Fayth,* the volume was intended for the use of Philip Howard and others who were in prison or who, for some reason, could not hear Mass or approach the Sacraments.

Naturally, Southwell was very tired by the time the book came off the press, for there had to be special care taken, not only that the printers avoid mistakes but also that they keep the whole proceeding secret. Sensible Father Garnet knew that the young priest needed a change and decided to send him on a journey.

"Father Robert, it is time for someone to visit Father Persons' old mother in Somerset; nobody has been there to take her Holy Communion in many weeks. Could you go?"

"Certainly, Father. You will stay in London?"

"Yes. If you make the expedition on horseback, you might call on your Catholic kin in Surrey, then go to Somerset, and finally make a wide swing to Worcestershire and Warwickshire. Close to Hinlip Hall, you will find a house with which you are not familiar, Baddesley Clinton. When you arrive there, give the name 'Cotton' to the gatekeeper. I left that as a password, knowing it was sometimes an alias of yours. Would you like companions for your ride? I am sure that Thomas and Henry Wiseman would be glad to escort you."

106

"Father, I am less conspicuous without an escort. I never forget Harry Vaux's being made prisoner when he protected me," replied Southwell.

Father Garnet looked up sympathetically. "I understand. Ride alone if you prefer. You know, of course, that Lady Katherine Copley has been released from Fleet Prison and is about to go into exile overseas?"

"Yes. I hope for a glimpse of her in Surrey."

"She will be glad to see you. God be with you. Forget books and printers' ink and the stench of London jails, and enjoy the fresh air and beautiful countryside."

So it was that a thin gentleman in dark riding clothes, with a hat pulled down over his head, rode through Warwickshire one green and gold autumn day. Lustrous clouds threw shadows on the yellowing fields; larks soared and sang. The fragrance of hay that was stacked beyond the trim hedges delighted the horseman and quickened the step of his chestnut mare.

There was not a dwelling in sight, but presently the rider saw in the distance a grove, and following a dirt road that was scarcely more than a track across a meadow, he guided his mare in the direction of the trees. A fenced paddock convinced him that he was taking the right route. When he reached the gate and was about to dismount to open it, an elderly countryman appeared like a gnome from the other side.

"You are for the great house, sir?"

"Yes. You can give the name 'Cotton.' I am expected, I believe."

"Yes, sir," said the old man, opening the gate. Then, when the rider and mare had passed through, he fastened it and turned. "There is another visitor still to come. If you will ride to yonder larch tree and follow the road to the left, you will soon see the house. A groom from the stable yard will take the mare."

The gentleman thanked the gatekeeper, rode on to the larch tree, and then followed the road to the house, which was visible as soon as he reached the top of a rise. It was a mansion of moderate size. Riding slowly, he saw that two wings were built onto the main structure in such a way that a court was enclosed on three sides. Then, to his surprise, he discovered that a moat surrounded the building.

"So this is Baddesley Clinton," he thought. "Father Garnet did not say for whom to ask."

Just then a young groom, freckle-faced and tousled, appeared as noiselessly as had the old gatekeeper. "It will be Mr. Cotton? Will you dismount, sir? I'll take the mare to the stable and follow with your kit. You will be staying the night, they say. The drawbridge yonder leads to the door, and the ladies are all inside unless perhaps young Miss has took herself to the paddock."

The rider, somewhat stiff, dismounted and walked to the drawbridge. He paused a moment to survey his whereabouts, noting the brick and stone dwelling and the deep shadow that it cast on the water of the moat. As he reached the middle of the drawbridge, a punt rounded a corner of the house. In the boat, controlling it with perfect ease, was a girl of about twelve, her curls tucked up over her ears and her russet skirt looped to give her freedom.

"Why, Father Southwell!" she exclaimed, as she neared the bridge. "The name was 'Cotton.' Why, you are Cotton, aren't you! Wait till I tie the punt, and I'll take you to Mother and Aunt Anne. We are here strictly incognito . . . Aunt Anne's idea or Father Garnet's. But Mother, that is, my cousin Mrs. Brooksby, has rented the house. She is so timid that nobody would dream that she would rent a country house for a refuge for Jesuits. But Aunt Anne is different."

As she talked, Frances got out of the punt, tied it to an iron ring, and scrambled up to the bridge, unlooping her skirt as she climbed. "Oh, I am so happy to see you. And you will never, never guess who is here. But I will tell you who is coming this evening, for I haven't promised to keep him a secret. It is Mr. William Byrd, the composer, and we shall have music."

Southwell said, "So we meet again, Frances. I hope this occasion will not be so exciting. It is rumored that your Uncle Harry Vaux is to be released from Fleet Prison; he will have been there a year in November, poor man."

"We call the Fleet our town house; you know Grandfather was there for a while, also. We thought that this would be a good place for Uncle Harry to get well." Then she rushed to the house door and entered, exclaiming, "Mother! Aunt Anne! Mr. Cotton is here, and you will never, never guess who he turned out to be!"

Southwell followed Frances into a room where two ladies were sitting by a window mending old vestments. They rose and greeted him, then instantly, as was second nature with Catholics, they and Frances knelt for his blessing.

"So I find the Ladies Vaux at Baddesley Clinton," remarked the priest, as they rose.

"Strictly incognito," Frances reminded him. "Mother, may I take him right away and show him the sacristy and the priest's room and the secret?"

Mrs. Brooksby smiled indulgently and Frances, her finger on her lips, tiptoed from the room, beckoning Southwell to follow into a dim hall at the end of which a door was ajar. He noticed that it was a heavy door with great iron bolts that seemed to be new. Frances, pausing an instant, gave it a push and whispered, "There is the secret."

They both peered into a shadowy room and for a moment Southwell thought there was nobody there. Then he saw, kneeling with rosary beads in his hands, the smallest man he had ever seen.

"This is the new sacristy," whispered Frances. "And the man is the secret. Guess who?"

"Brother Nicholas Owen," guessed Southwell.

" 'Little John,' Father Garnet calls him. And you will never, never guess why he is here." Frances coughed, and said, "Watch him."

Brother Nicholas glanced toward the door, rose, and came over to them.

"Mr. Cotton," said Frances, "this is our builder. Having taken a house in the country, we found it necessary to make some repairs. . . . Oh, Brother Nicholas, may I show him?"

"I thought it would be you, Father Robert," said the lay brother. "Naturally, you know why I am here. The work was finished yesterday. And I linger, awaiting Father Garnet's orders."

"But may I show him?" demanded Frances again.

"We will go together, young lady," replied Brother Nicholas. "You know, Father Robert, that it is a matter of principle with me never to exhibit my work or even refer indirectly to it lest I betray something, give a clue. But . . . but circumstances were against me in this instance. As you might guess, no hiding place at Baddesley Clinton could be hidden from Miss Frances Burrows."

"She can outwit pursuivants," said Southwell. "I have reason to know."

Frances had darted ahead into the next room, raised the lid of a window seat, climbed inside, and disappeared. Brother Nicholas directed Southwell to the spot and motioned to him to follow Frances, while he himself went last and closed the opening by which they had reached a tunnel that ran parallel with the moat. A short distance from where they stood there was a shaft from the new sacristy, and a heavy stone slab that could be raised and lowered like a portcullis.

Frances called Southwell's attention to the slab, explaining, "It has a counterbalancing weight concealed in the wall. That is part of our repairs. Do you see all that rubble up there, Father? When I was in the punt just now, I was looking to make sure that it blocked the loopholes. Nobody would know from the outside, Little John. I mean, Brother Nicholas. Come, Father, there is something else for you to see."

While Brother Nicholas was giving Southwell a rough idea of how he had utilized the original drainage system for the tunnel and had made new drains, Frances was hastening back up through the window seat and beckoning them to follow. When they were all in the sacristy again, she fetched a stool, climbed on it, and hoisted herself through a cleverly concealed trap door in the ceiling. "Come on, Father! Want a hand? Brother Nicholas can get up without a stool. He is like a squirrel."

When Southwell got through, Frances was already well ahead of him, going from one attic joist to another, avoiding huge beams, swinging along as easily as a spider. They finally reached the roof and the chimneys. Frances got down on hands and knees and crawled into what seemed to be a hole. Southwell followed and in a moment found he could rise to his feet in a small room that had two benches on each side. Frances, breathless, was sitting on one.

Brother Nicholas called from the roof, "Rest a moment, Father!"

Southwell, thankful to take his advice, seated himself on the bench opposite Frances.

Suddenly Frances said, "Father, what is a Mother Superior?"

Taken aback by the question, Southwell parried, "Something like a Lady Prioress. Why do you ask?"

"Because Father Garnet said that if it turned out that I had a vocation to be a nun, I'd need a quick Mother Superior. You have cobwebs in your hair, so I think that we must hurry down so you can wash before supper. Shall I go first?"

"You usually do," replied Southwell laughing, as she lowered herself to the floor and crawled out onto the roof again. "Six priests could sit here if necessary," he thought, surveying the tiny refuge. "I suppose Baddesley Clinton has been readied for our semi-annual meetings."

Chapter 18

Lord Burghley wanted Catholics declared traitors without the use of the harsh Act of 1585. His idea was to trap them by requiring them to swear to their reply to what became known as the "Bloody Question."

"Do you recognize Queen Elizabeth as the lawful Queen of England?" a recusant would be asked.

"I do," the recusant would reply.

"What would you do if the Pope were to send over an army and declare that his only object was to bring the kingdom back to its Catholic allegiance? And if he stated at the same time that there was no other way of re-establishing the Catholic faith, and commanded everyone by his apostolic authority to support him? Whose side would you be on then, the Pope's or the Queen's?"

The intention of the questioners was, of course, to make a

Catholic seem to choose between loyalty to the Pope, whom he knew to be God's representative on earth, and loyalty to England, his beloved country.

The English lawyers, even those who hated Catholics, told Lord Burghley that it was an unfair question. And when Southwell wrote to the Father General describing it, he said that the Catholic prisoners were "examined not simply about what they have done, but about what they would be likely to do . . . what intentions they would have if this or that were to occur."

The English Jesuits loved England. They were risking martyrdom for their Catholic countrymen, and they felt that they must help in this dilemma. Father Garnet, Father Southwell and other priests met with Catholic laymen to decide how recusants, loyal to both the Pope and the Queen, could answer truthfully if questioned by the Government. They came to the conclusion that Catholics should reply gently, without bitterness, affirming their loyalty to their Queen and Country. Since there was no question of the Faith at stake, and since their answers might turn to the ruin of the whole group, the priests were to reply that they were in Holy Orders and so forbidden warfare, but that they would pray God to aid the side of justice. The laymen were to pledge themselves against all unjust aggressors, whoever they might be.

Good Catholics were grateful to their spiritual advisers for wording brief answers to the Bloody Question, and for the assurance that they could with clear consciences defend their country.

In the year 1588, the Bloody Question was a heart-rending one. Although Sir Francis Drake, when he had raided Cadiz in the spring of 1587, destroyed much of King Philip II's shipping, a vast fleet or Armada was being built by the Spanish and made ready to attack England in the spring of 1588. Now that the Queen of Scots was dead, King Philip II claimed to be the rightful heir to the English throne. He had asked the Pope to share the expense of equipping an army. This had been refused. But he had received a promise that the Pope would give financial assistance, should Philip be successful in getting possession of an English port.

It began to seem as if Catholics would be put to a very hard test and so, once the answers to the Bloody Question were decided upon, Father Garnet called Southwell to him.

"You have many friends in Sussex and Hampshire, Father Robert. Would you like to visit them?"

Southwell knew that this was his Superior's manner of ordering him on a horseback journey to places frequented by recusants and to the very districts where the Spaniards might attempt to land. He gladly agreed to go.

When he rode out of Southwark, he headed due south. The distance to Portsmouth was about sixty miles. He looked forward to visiting scenes familiar to him in his boyhood when he had stayed with his cousins. He would go to Gatton, where the Copleys had lived; to Roughey, his mother's childhood home; to Philip Howard's Arundel Castle, and to his cousin George Cotton's place at Warblington. Perhaps he would see the creek from which he and John Cotton had slipped away to France. Probably he would see John Cotton himself, and possibly some of the Gages and Banisters. There was a faint chance that he might see his sister Mary, for her husband's old home, Idsworth, was only a few miles from Warblington; Edward Banister might have taken Mary there from the London heat. Wherever he turned in Sussex and Hampshire, he would be among friends and kin.

As he rode along, he recalled landing on the Channel coast, two years previously, all afire with the desire for martyrdom. Now he was thankful to live or die as God willed. In 1586, the villages through which he had passed were sleepy, humdrum places. Now, in 1588, they were stirred to excitement by circular letters that had gone forth from the Queen to the lord lieutenants of the counties calling for horsemen and foot soldiers, for small vessels and seamen. Word had spread that King Philip's fleet might sail from Spain any day and attempt landings on the coast. Once already Spanish galleons had set sail and had had to put back because of a storm. And a storm had overtaken Lord Howard and Sir Francis Drake when they sailed toward Spain; they had returned to the Channel and were waiting in Plymouth.

Whenever Southwell stopped to rest and water his mare, he saw men drilling, for the response to the call for defense had been quick. He heard bits of rumor.

"The Prince of Parma has an army of 30,000 waiting near Dunkirk to cross on flatboats to the Thames," one rider told another.

"The Spanish Admiral has 64 galleons provisioned and many galleys well manned, while we have but 36 vessels in our Royal Navy."

"But hundreds of small vessels are being equipped and manned by volunteers. And we have Lord Howard and Drake and Hawkins, and the captain Sir Robert Southwell," boasted another rider.

"Their Admiral is weak," someone asserted.

"They say that the Prince of Parma is the world's cleverest general," countered another, "and our army's leader, the Earl of Leicester, is a stupid fop and—"

"Sh-h-h. Quiet! He is a favorite with Her Majesty," warned an elderly yeoman.

"And if we do not let them land, we will not need our army. Sir Walter Raleigh insists that we will gain by defending rather than attacking. . . ."

"We can trust Lord Howard for that. I'll wager Sir Francis Drake will have a whack at the Spaniards."

So the talk ran, and Southwell, quiet, inconspicuous as always, lingered in the background and listened.

He spent the first night with a recusant family and after early Mass the following morning rode on.

Green fields spread beneath a cloud-strewn blue sky. Birds sang in the hedges, and rabbits scurried across his path to roadside ditches. He found himself noticing the plants familiar to him in boyhood, the stone fern, fennel, vetch and mullein, and the wild flowers in which the southeast counties abound. All nature seemed at peace. Yet a great encounter was in the making, he was sure. England and Spain would finally clash. Two procrastinators, Elizabeth and Philip, would join battle.

He rode through Sussex making the necessary calls on the recusant families. It was several days before he crossed into Hampshire. Then he knew where he was by the marshes with their rushes and mallows and burdock and bindweed growing along the road. Finally, he rode into the small town of Havant. Here, very cautiously, he made inquiry in the market place about Warblington.

"Yes, sir. The family is at the manor," he was informed by a carter.

"And there they stay. They're Papists," put in a surly idler.

"Not a mile from the house do they stir," added a laborer.

"I am looking for the former seat of the Earls of Salisbury," explained Southwell, drawing the carter's attention.

"A long time ago, that was. It is the Cottons of Warblington that be there now. You are a stranger in these parts?" the laborer asked.

Southwell smiled. He leaned over and pressed something into the carter's hand. Their eyes met, but not a glance betrayed that the horseman and carter remembered each other from boyhood. The carter, like many of the Cottons' country neighbors, was a loyal Catholic.

"Your way lies yonder," he said, pointing out a road that he well knew was familiar to the rider.

"Thank you," said Southwell, and turned toward Warblington.

As he approached a narrow bridge near the house, he saw a gentleman directing several old laborers who were spreading gravel. He reined in, exclaiming, "John!"

"Robert!" replied his cousin, coming to him. "Well met. We were expecting you." He turned to a workman with the order, "Call a stable boy," and then explained: "Most of the men have gone. We are mustering troops, you know. When did you leave London?"

"Several days ago. I came down through Gatton and Horsham," replied Southwell.

"Yes, I know. We Hampshire recusants have a communications system. Come, dismount. Give me your kit. The boy will take your mare for a good rubbing. Stiff? It seems a long time since we climbed the North Tower of Notre Dame in Paris."

"Eleven years."

"Eleven long years. And now you are a Jesuit. And I am a very poor cousin." John laughed gently. "We pay everything we have in fines: fines for not going to the Queen's services, for hearing Mass, for anything you can think of. If we don't pay the fines, the Crown may seize and enjoy our goods and chattels, two thirds of our land, and goodness knows what!"

"But you have kept the Faith," said Southwell.

"Most of us, with the exception of our cousin Henry Cotton. He is the Queen's godson, and an Oxford man. They say that he will be Protestant Bishop of Salisbury some day."

"Cousin George and Cousin Mary are here?"

"Yes. Father was in the Fleet Prison for a long time, you know."

"Yes. My Aunt Katherine Copley was there, also. And Harry Vaux. Harry's cousin, Frances Burrows, says that they call the Fleet their town house," said Southwell, as a stable boy appeared and he dismounted, handing over the reins.

John Cotton smiled. "But members of our family put up at the Marshalsea as well."

"All better than the Counter-in-the-Poultry. By the way, little Brother Ralph has been moved from there to the Clink."

"Good!" John Cotton's eyes twinkled. "On the bank of the Thames. Closer to the river for book-running. My, what an exciting time we had smuggling the Bible in!"

They were walking toward the house, and Southwell was relishing the feel of soft turf and the sweet scents coming from the garden.

Cotton looked at him a moment, and then said, "There is a rumor that Lord Burghley's spies got hold of some printed sheets purporting to be instructions for English Catholics to rally to the Prince of Parma should he land with an army."

Southwell gasped, and exclaimed, "Can that be true!"

"I fear it is, Robert. Worse still, the instructions are said to be the work of our old friend Dr. Allen, now a Roman Cardinal."

His companion sighed. "He and Father Persons have lived abroad too long. I fear they are out of touch with actual life in England. How do you feel about the expected invasion?"

"I stand by the Church. And I stand by England," answered Cotton immediately. "The Bloody Question is hypothetical. The Pope has not told us to choose between the Papacy and our country."

"That is so, of course. But these instructions play into Lord Burghley's hand. God willing, the Prince of Parma will not land!"

The two cousins were grave as they went on through the

118

garden to the green courtyard. When a few minutes later they were in the great hall, being greeted by the older Cottons, Southwell was still feeling the shock of his cousin's revelation about Cardinal Allen's instructions. Here he was in the beautiful old house, with its large hall and long gallery; here, at last, was a real chapel, not a cramped, hidden Mass-chamber. And he was with his own kin. Yet his mind was occupied with one idea. What would the Catholics suffer when the Spanish were repulsed? He did not doubt for a minute that the English would win.

It was fortunate that his thoughts were diverted somewhat by the arrival of many guests. Not all at one time, but by twos and threes they came all through the afternoon. They were prepared to stay the night and hear Mass the following morning. Edward and Mary Banister rode over from Idsworth. Margaret Copley Gage and her husband arrived from Roughey. There were Shelleys and Listers, Gunters, Wriothesleys, Brownes, Sackvilles, Uvedales, and there was more noise than Southwell had heard since the clatter of pots and pans in his Roman novitiate.

"Oh, Margaret!" exclaimed Mary Banister, embracing her cousin.

"Oh, Mary!" replied Margaret Gage, kissing Mary's pink cheek. "The last time I saw you, I was a prisoner in the Fleet. My mother, by the way, has reached France."

"And where is your brother Anthony?" someone asked.

"Who knows?" said Margaret. "He is no longer the Pope's guest in Rome, as Cousin Robert will tell you."

"Writing verse somewhere, no doubt," suggested Edward Banister.

"Not in prison," asserted Mary, her blue eyes dancing. "Not our Anthony. Margaret is the family prisoner."

"Lord Howard of Effingham doesn't let Margaret stay in

prison. With his daughter married to Sir Robert Southwell, what kin is the Admiral-in-Chief of the Royal Navy to the Wily Jesuit of Warblington? Now, Cousin Robert, don't protest; wily and Warblington are alliterative," said John Copley.

"Have you dangerous Jesuits a scheme for our behavior in the Armada crisis?" asked John Gage, half in earnest.

"To speak truth, we have, and divulging it to all of you is my mission here," replied Southwell. Then he gave them an account of the London meeting, and the conclusions reached there.

"At least we know what to say if anyone stops to ask us. They tell me that Sir Francis Walsingham is on his last legs now that he has disposed of the Queen of Scots. But that fellow Topcliffe, the torturer, is working his way into Her Majesty's favor," said John Gage.

"Whatever Catholics answer, that fiend tortures. Someone told me—"

"Mary will have to lure him away from the Scavenger's Daughter," Margaret Gage interrupted, lest some of Topcliffe's hideous methods of torture be mentioned. "Mary can get around any pursuivant or jailer."

"Not Topcliffe," John Cotton disagreed. "Pray God to deliver us all from him."

"They say that if the weather holds, the Spanish Fleet with Medina Sidonia in command will certainly sail soon," one of the Sackville men said.

Then they began to discuss their preparations on the coast, the numerous small vessels that they had had made ready for the defense, the mustering of men on their estates. Southwell listened and, weary from his journey and alarmed by what lay in store for recusants, he was greatly relieved when Mary beckoned him to the chapel to superintend preparations for the next day's Mass.

Before light the following morning, he had heard the confessions of the guests and the tenants, said Mass and given Holy Communion. And before any guest had left, he had taken the road toward London.

Several days later, as he rode into the city, Queen Elizabeth was setting out for Tilbury to address the troops gathered there to defend the realm. After a short wait came word that the mighty Spanish galleons, harassed by the small English vessels, had anchored in Calais roads. Parma's flotilla had been blockaded by Dutch vessels. Then word came that Lord Howard, who could not attack directly, had had eight old wooden ships soaked in oil, set ablaze, and let loose. The commanders of the galleons, endangered by the flames, cut their cables and put out to sea. Sir Robert Southwell and the other captains attacked. Lord Howard and Sir Francis Drake pursued. A mighty storm came up. The Spanish ships, tossed by the winds and waves, rounded Scotland, but some were driven onto the rocks of the Irish coast and lost there. An English squadron had been stationed to prevent Parma's crossing the Channel. Parma did not try. An astute general, he knew that Spain had lost the Battle of the Armada to England.

When word of the enemy's defeat reached Southwell, he knelt on the floor in his small room in Arundel House and prayed. Better than anyone he knew that the Government would now turn on the Catholics. They must make ready to die for the Faith.

Chapter 19

The first rays of the sun came through the high window and lighted Christopher Buxton's cell in the Marshalsea Prison.

Kneeling in a corner close to the prisoner's pallet, a heavy dark coat around his shoulders to protect him from the September cold, was Southwell. Close enough to touch, standing in front of a plain deal table on which were altar cloths, missal, altar cards and a covered chalice, was young Father Christopher Buxton.

Southwell had said Mass very early at Lord Montague's house and had come from there to the nearby Marshalsea to serve Christopher Buxton's last Mass. This former pupil of his had been arrested in Kent soon after he arrived in England from Rome and after a long stay in prison had now been condemned to be hanged for his Faith at Canterbury. His face shone above his threadbare vestments, and his voice was clear and firm as he uttered in Latin the psalm that the priest says at the foot of the altar.

"Judge me, O God and distinguish my cause from the nation that is not holy; deliver me from the unjust and deceitful man," said the young priest.

"For Thou, O God, art my strength; why dost Thou cast me off? And why go I sorrowful, the enemy afflicting me?" responded Southwell.

"Send forth Thy light and Thy truth; they have led me, and brought me unto Thy holy hill, and into Thy tabernacles," continued the celebrant.

"And I will go unto the altar of God, to God who giveth joy to my youth," said Southwell.

The sound of a half-stifled sob startled Southwell. Then he realized that others were hearing this Mass through a hole in the wall to the next cell, and that an older man there was thinking of the priest as too young for martyrdom. Indeed, it was well known that Buxton's being so young and handsome had softened the hearts of those at his trial, and that he had been entreated to conform and save his life.

Southwell's heart was breaking. He had taught Buxton in Rome. Now he was joining him in offering the Sacrifice that would prepare him for his own sacrifice at Canterbury whither he was to be led to die. Since the executions that followed on the Armada, London had reeked with martyrs' blood and the populace wanted no more hangings at Tyburn, so Canterbury and other cities were chosen.

"I confess to Almighty God . . ." the priest began the *Confiteor* and went on to the end. In turn, Southwell repeated the prayer.

As the Mass progressed the sun brightened, sending a shaft of light on the young priest's hands. When the words of the Consecration had been spoken, and the Host was raised aloft, there was an exclamation in English from someone on the other side of the partition: "My Lord and my God!" Evidently the speaker had seen how brilliantly white the Host was in the sunlight.

"Lord, it is good for us to be here," thought Southwell, adoring. When the time for the Communion of the laity came, he accompanied the celebrant to the opening in the wall. For the last time, the English priest who had spent his youth preparing to serve English Catholics was giving them the Bread of Life. He was twenty-six years old.

When Mass was finished, Southwell handed the missal and chalice and altar cloths to someone in the next cell, made another trip to the opening with the vestments that Buxton had removed, and closed the slide and covered it. While his young friend made his thanksgiving on his knees, he seated himself on a low stool and took advantage of the light to read his breviary.

Presently a wooden bowl of porridge and a hunk of bread were shoved into the cell by a jailer. Buxton rose, smiling, and asked, "Will you share my porridge, Father Robert?"

"Gladly," replied Southwell.

The prisoner seated himself on his pallet, drew an earthenware dish from a low shelf, and divided the contents of the bowl.

"A message came through to me from your friend Father Philip Neri," said Buxton. "He sent me his blessing."

"I was thinking of the day you and Christopher Bales and I went to his roof-top room to read him the account of George Haydock's martyrdom," said Southwell.

"So was I. And I was thinking that, whereas I leave England for Heaven by way of Canterbury this week, the other Christopher will soon arrive in England, probably by some northern port. He will do more than fill my place. I have never known a holier man than Christopher Bales. He is a little younger than I, you know, and there had to be a special dispensation for him to be ordained."

"I recall how white he was that day in Father Philip's room," said Southwell.

"We thought his pallor due to his excitement over the account that you read. But, in fact, the Roman climate was making him ill, and he was sent back to Rheims before he was ordained."

"So I heard. You saw him when you were on your way to England?"

"Yes. Such a journey from Rome to Rheims! And while everyone was telling us that we must not try to come to England, the one thing that gave us concern was our failure to sell our horse. We had spent all our money, and wanted the price of the sale to get here." Buxton laughed merrily.

Southwell remembered Christopher's habitual cool determination. "But you got here!"

"In spite of another friend of yours; Dr. Darbyshire tried to prevent me. We saw him in France just after the Queen of Scots was executed. He said that I was young and inexperienced and would be captured." Buxton laughed aloud. "I thought him overcautious. But he was a prophet.

"I want your blessing, by the way . . . now, before they come to conduct me to Canterbury." The young priest took Southwell's empty porridge dish and put it with the wooden bowl, saying, "A present for the jailer. I shall not need it again."

Then he knelt quietly beside Southwell, who rose and blessed him.

"Thank you, Father Robert. Now, one more favor." He put his hand under his pallet and brought forth a manuscript. "This is a *Rituale* that I have copied while here in prison." He handed Southwell the sheets on which he had copied all of the services of the Church that a priest needs that are not in the Missal or Breviary. Then he seated himself on his pallet again and said, "You have been suffering with others, Father Robert."

"For months. All summer the executioners were busy. There were so many Catholics to be executed that they were taken in carts, not dragged on hurdles. One of the martyrs was that Margaret Ward whose crime was furnishing a priest with a rope for his escape from Bridewell. She was jubilant because she had helped a priest to freedom."

"I wonder if there will be as many martyrs now that the Earl of Leicester is dead. God rest his soul." Buxton made the Sign of the Cross. He was referring to the very recent death of Robert Dudley, Queen Elizabeth's favorite.

"God only knows. That we English Catholics should be persecuted by other Englishmen adds shame for our fellow countrymen to our other sufferings, doesn't it? I explained to Father General Aquaviva, when I wrote to him several weeks ago, that the fury and cruelty must not be regarded as a disgrace to our nation but as the outcome of a pestilent heresy. Our ignorant rulers deserve our pity."

Just then there was the clank of chains at the door. Both men rose. Neither spoke to the other. While Buxton courteously greeted the guard come to conduct him to the scaffold at Canterbury, the gentleman in the dark cloak put on his hat, pulled it down to hide his face as much as possible, and slipped through the door. Seemingly he was absorbed by the darkness of the corridor. As he stepped into the street, he noticed that the sun that had shone into the cell was shrouded and that a cold autumn drizzle had begun.

"Another English martyr for Canterbury," thought Southwell. "One quite as brave as Thomas à Becket."

Chapter 20

In the spring of 1589, the gardens at Arundel House were lovely. Part of the mansion was occupied by those in favor with the Queen, and there was every reason for the gardeners to please their fancy. By mid-April, yellow primroses and purple violets were in bloom.

Walking up and down, pausing now and then to notice the glow of the primroses in the sun and to enjoy the violets' fragrance, was a slender gentleman who wore somber clothing. He seemed perfectly at home, and was examining a rose bush that gave promise of blossom when a nurse and a little curly-headed boy of about three came around the corner of a maze. The child, with a happy shout, ran to the gentleman, who swung him to his shoulder.

"Piggy-back, please. Piggy-back, please," begged the little one.

"Well, I never!" exclaimed Melissa.

Southwell shifted the small heir to the House of Norfolk to a riding position, the tiny legs around his neck.

"It is as good a disguise as any, I suppose," admitted Melissa. "Certainly no boatmen would expect a Jesuit to arrive at the water steps with a wee lad pulling his hat down. Now, don't push his hat off, my little one; pull it on till it sticks. There's likely to be a rabble of curious busybodies at our landing stairs this morning."

Carrying Thomas, the child born after Philip Howard's arrest, Southwell took the path that led through the garden to the private dock on the Thames. The small boy did not know that his father was to be sentenced at Westminster Hall that day, and that the chaplain was on his way to watch his exit from the court and to return as promptly as possible to Countess Anne to report on the fate of her husband. Almost four years had passed since the Earl was captured, sentenced to imprisonment at the Queen's pleasure and a fine of ten thousand pounds. Since then he had been in the Tower of London, but this morning he had been taken by boat from the Water Gate there to the landing stairs near Westminster Hall, and from there to the tribunal. It was Melissa's idea that South-well's best means of reaching the scene of her master's trial would be to mingle with the excitement-seekers who would throng the Thames in the hope of seeing the Earl. The London mobs, tired of bloodshed, were eager for fresh diversion; the sight of the First Lord of the Realm, a descendant of King Edward the Confessor, would be interesting. He had been accused of having prayed for the success of those who tried to invade England.

Southwell, approaching the Arundel House landing stairs with the child on his shoulders, broke into a gentle trot.

"Who-a, who-a," cautioned his rider, and he slowed up obediently.

Melissa, who had been walking behind, came abreast of the two and Southwell swung the small boy to her arms. She beckoned with her head, indicating the boats bobbing in the water. A swarthy boatman, with rings in his ears and a blue kerchief wound around his head pirate-fashion, brought his boat close to the water steps. His action was evidently pre-arranged, for she addressed him immediately. She stood on the wet steps against which the dirty river water lapped, holding the struggling child in her arms, and gave directions. "His Lordship is a stranger in these parts, Michael. You are to show him the sights of London. And whatever you do, don't fail to go upstream first, toward Westminster."

Michael touched his forehead in agreement, then steadied his swaying rowboat with a boat hook. Southwell descended the landing stairs and stepped in. Instantly the oarsman shoved away from the landing, and rowing forcefully, headed up-stream. So quick had the embarkation been that the non-descript rivermen and their passengers who were close to the steps scarcely noticed it, their attention having been drawn to a curly-haired small boy who was attempting to free himself from his nurse's grasp. They were in good humor, roughly applauding the child's efforts and taunting his nurse. Needless to say, Melissa prolonged the entertainment.

As Michael swung his boat out into the river, Southwell smiled and eased the hat that Philip's heir had pushed on all too firmly. He thought of the child's lot. His great-grandfather and his grandfather were beheaded. What of his father? Perhaps the day would tell.

With only one passenger, the blue-kerchiefed Michael was making good progress, with a strong and steady pull on his oars. Southwell was sure that no matter how dense the river traffic became, they would be at Westminster in time to be among the first to know the results of the trial. He thought that it seemed strange that he should be destined to mingle in a rabble for news of one whose spiritual life he had been directing by letter for several years. Never had he even glimpsed Philip Howard. That very morning, after early Mass at Arundel House, he had paused and studied the portrait that the Court artist Zucchero, who had painted Queen Elizabeth, had made of the Earl. It showed him as tall, dark, with a gentle pensive face that seemed shadowed by sorrow. Although he had posed when he was a pleasure-seeking courtier, the tragedy of his youth, his father's execution for treason when he was fifteen, marked his expression. How would he look when he came out of court with the edge of the axe turned toward him or away from him to indicate his fate?

Southwell let his attention wander to the passengers in the many craft headed upstream. Doubtless others were thinking of the Earl. The humor abroad seemed a good omen, and he felt almost as certain as the London people did that the edge of the axe would be turned away. After all, what wrong had Philip done the Queen? It was true that he, who had been baptized a Catholic in infancy, had the King of Spain for a godfather. That was not his fault. He had not been instructed in his religion except perhaps in his earliest childhood when Dr. Gregory Martin was his tutor. He had behaved as a Protestant at Cambridge where he studied, and then at Court. Only when he had been converted by Campion's bravery had he asked Father William Weston to reconcile him to the Church.

Southwell pondered the matter as he had many times before. Probably the letter that Philip had left with his sister, Lady Margaret Sackville, to be delivered to the Queen after his escape to France was too frankly worded. The letter had been seized after his capture, and Lord Burghley and Queen Elizabeth might well have made wry faces when they read his explanations for his attempt to leave England; he mentioned not only his Catholic religion, but also the fact that both his poet grandfather, the Earl of Surrey, and his father the Duke of Norfolk, had been beheaded by their sovereigns. The Earl of Surrey had dared display royal arms to which he had a perfect right; the Tudors did not relish the Howards' rank. His father had planned to marry the Queen of Scots. And he? Confined in the Lanthorn Tower of the Tower of London, he had contrived to have a fellow prisoner, old Father Bennet, celebrate Mass. He had served the Mass, at which Sir Thomas Gerard, Father John Gerard's father, had been present.

Thinking of that happening, Southwell shuddered. John Gerard, who had been confined in the Marshalsea Prison when a lad, had now come back to London with another Jesuit, Father Oldcorne, and Father Christopher Bales, and about the first news he heard was that his father had betrayed the Earl of Arundel. Poor old Father Bennet had wavered in his testimony, and the spy who had been stationed in the Tower to inform had told of Philip's serving Mass.

Southwell shaded his eyes with his hand, and gazed on the shimmering river. White gulls swirled and swooped, coming

130

down with raucous screams of hunger to pounce on refuse that
floated on the water. The boats were more numerous now and
the traffic was becoming noisy with the shouts of rivermen,
the clash of oars, and the splash from passing barges. A gaily
bedecked barge passed, and the sound of music and women's
laughter reached him. Philip Howard's early companions at
Court might be aboard, he thought. They liked Philip well
enough, but Lord Burghley, whose ward he had been, now
seemed to hate him. And the Queen? Who knew? The Howards
were too high born to please either the Sovereign or her
Secretary.

For what was Philip being tried? Southwell asked himself
again. "For having favored the excommunication of the Queen
and having prayed for the invaders." Of course, the Pope's
Bill of Excommunication had never been formally published
in England. As for praying for the success of the Armada?
Southwell, thinking of this, sighed, for one of the matters of
conscience on which Philip had managed to convey his doubts
to his chaplain was the thought that, deep down in his heart,
he suspected himself of sympathy with the cause of his Catholic godfather, the King of Spain. Had Philip II's troops landed
and been victorious, Philip Howard, the Queen's prisoner,
would have been freed, his title and possessions restored to
him, and better still, he would have had full right to practice
his Catholic religion. Southwell's thoughts harked back to
Ralph Sherwin's exclamation when he and Edmund Campion
were tried: "The plain reason for our standing here is religion,
not treason." If a man could be condemned to the death of a
traitor for what he believed or prayed, then the Earl of Arundel might become a martyr.

Michael was now skillfully guiding his rowboat through the
boats and barges, the mass of varied shipping, that neared
the Westminster wharf and landing stairs. Southwell saw that

the banks of the Thames were thronged. He noted the tense silence of the crowd, then with a prayer looked away from the shore to the white clouds that sailed across a deep blue sky. Suddenly a loud cry of indignation broke out, for on a wave of words hurled from one bystander to another the sentence had traveled. Those within sight had shouted that the edge of the axe was toward the Earl. He had been condemned to the death of a traitor: to be hanged, drawn and quartered.

"Condemned!" called a sinewy waterman to Michael.

For the first time Michael's eyes met Southwell's. "To Arundel House with the current, your Lordship?" demanded the boatman, starting to head his boat downstream, his strong arms managing the heavy oars.

"Yes, to Arundel House," replied the priest. Praying God's help for Philip and his Countess, he found himself comforted by lines from a poem that the Earl had written in the Tower and sent to him. The lines were addressed to Christ:

> "The hope, the life, the only help
> Of such as trust in Thee."

Southwell realized that Philip had no illusions, that he knew that his only hope was in Christ.

Chapter 21

One evening soon after Christmas, when gusts of wind were whirling bits of paper and straw through the cold air, Southwell walked up Chancery Lane toward Gray's Inn, from which he planned to take a familiar passage into Gray's Inn Road. Pulling his cloak around him, he walked very fast. As he strode along, several subjects were uppermost in his mind. Philip Howard was still alive, and he was thinking that there must be truth in the Court rumor whispered to the Countess of Arundel that Queen Elizabeth would not have the Earl executed. And Southwell was marveling that he himself continued to elude Richard Topcliffe's searchers. It was exciting to know that the priest-hunter was particularly enraged with him and scoured the streets of London and his cousins' estates in Sussex and Hampshire for "Robert Southwell, alias Cotton, infamous Jesuit and Priest."

Southwell, thinking of Topcliffe, quickened his pace and drew his dark cloak tighter as if to make himself even less conspicuous in the dusk. How had Topcliffe come to such power? he wondered. It was true that he had been in Lord Burghley's service for years, and that although he had no title and was simply known as "one of Her Majesty's servants," he was a favorite with Queen Elizabeth. He was ugly, past middle age, cruel beyond compare, yet the Queen received him and listened to him; the very judges in court hesitated to reprimand him when he hauled in Catholic prisoners and shouted imprecations. The Queen's shrewd Secretary, Sir Francis Walsingham, had had a certain dignity, and had hooded his ruffian spies with a semblance of law. But this Topcliffe enjoyed taking part in a search or in joining a brawl when a recusant was arrested. He set his seemingly insane mind to the invention of tortures, and a term for his attentions had come into use, a coined word that looked like an Italian verb: *topcliffizzare.*

Southwell shuddered at the thought of the tyrant's favorite method for trying to extract from a recusant prisoner accounts of his movements. He would have his victim hung by his

133

wrists against a wall, his feet not touching the ground. Circulation was impaired and the sufferings were somewhat like those produced by crucifixion. When the victim began to lose consciousness, a stool was pushed under his feet just long enough to restore him and extend his agony. In Topcliffe's estimation, the great advantage in this method of torture was **that it** could be done privately in his own dwelling without resort to the racks in the Torture Chamber in the Tower of London; the public had had enough of the horrors of the Scavenger's Daughter. Then, too, after a prisoner was taken down from the wall, there were no broken bones as sure evidences of his hideous pain.

Southwell was still considering the recusant's plight when he reached Gray's Inn, but there his thoughts were pleasantly interrupted by a tumult of blithe voices. Rushing toward him came a horde of young men, their wild laughter piercing the evening air. He recalled that it was near Twelfth Night, the season of revels, and that these merrymakers must be coming from the great Hall where masques were staged for royalty. The Queen delighted in a masque. He smiled and stood back against a railing to let the crowd pass. As he did so, he almost collided with a sinister-looking individual, whose gimlet eyes scanned stragglers who emerged from the Hall. Southwell stepped aside quickly and entered the passage he sought. Was that a spy set there to watch for Catholic youths who could not be dissuaded from frequenting the Inns of Court? For instance, young Thomas Wiseman and his brother lodged near here, and were forever offering to escort priests on their country missions. Perhaps it was natural that Christopher Bales, when he had arrived in London shortly after Christopher Buxton's execution, a little over a year ago, should have elected to dwell in Gray's Inn Road.

Southwell was on his way to Bales' lodging. The young

priest, who had been his student at the English College in Rome, had not been well, and he had been urging him to wear warmer clothing and to try to cure a persistent cough; he wanted to be sure that his advice had been heeded. Following the passage, he came to a shadowy alley, made a sharp turn, and opened a door that led directly into a ground floor corridor. Accustomed to darkness, he made his way cautiously to an inner door and rapped gently four times. He was admitted by a gaunt man whom he supposed to be Alexander Blake, with whom Christopher dwelt.

He surveyed the room as he greeted Blake. It was low ceilinged. Candles were burning, and there was a brazier filled with warm coals that gave off some heat. Standing close to the brazier, being fitted to a jerkin by a quick-motioned tailor, was Christopher Bales. The tailor measured and snipped, pinned and basted, but the young priest seemed completely absorbed in his thoughts, and the thin pale face on which the candlelight played wore an expression of indescribable peace. Then, spying his caller, Christopher greeted him cordially.

"Welcome, Father Robert! You find me obedient, letting myself be decked out like a peacock. Blake keeps the fire going to make me warm, and good Nick Horner endeavors to make me beautiful. And my cough is already much better."

Southwell acknowledged the greetings of all, and then reached over and touched the stuff from which Horner had cut the jerkin. "More like a robin than a peacock," he said, referring to the maroon shade.

"It is warm, sir. The warmest I could find," explained the tailor. "Father Bales objected to the color. But he would be too conspicuous among the young men did he wear a somber jerkin."

"And our Christopher is even now very young," said Southwell teasingly. "I understand that you got a dispensation to be ordained when you were under age, on your plea that you thought your health might benefit by your return to your native land, and that you might possibly do some good there?"

The young priest blushed. "Yes, Father. That is what I wrote Father Rector from Rheims. But the dispensation was already on the way," he replied.

"Would you have a cup of canary, Father, or muscadel?" asked Blake, remembering his duties as a host.

"No, no, thank you. I cannot tarry. I wanted to make sure that my young friend was provided against the cold. I see that he is: a warm jerkin, a warm brazier, and very warm hearts to cheer him." He started to turn to the door, but was recalled by the three men, who, in the midst of cloth scraps, tailor's shears, chalk, cutting board and all the paraphernalia of a fitting, knelt on the floor.

"Your blessing, Father," they insisted.

When Southwell had blessed them, he remembered the gimlet-eyed stranger who had been lingering at the entrance to their passage, and he cautioned the tailor, "When you depart for home, be careful. There may be a searcher in the neighborhood; I almost tripped over him."

Christopher Bales laughed and said, "To quote Sir Francis Walsingham's description, 'a priest of middle stature, auburn haired, beardless, and wont to go appareled in black.' Maybe it was Topcliffe himself looking for you!"

Southwell pulled his hat down firmly over his auburn hair and said, "I begin to think that he is color blind." With a wave to the tailor and Father Bales and a smile for Blake, who opened the door for him, he went out into the dark.

For the next few weeks, whenever Southwell thought of Christopher Bales, he pictured him not only as he appeared in Father Neri's roof-top room in Rome but also as he looked when he stood in his maroon jerkin in Blake's candlelit London chamber. It was a comfort to think of him among kind friends. But the pleasant picture did not last long, for one morning when he was busy writing, Melissa entered and handed him a rough, dirty sheet of paper. She had appeared from nowhere, as was her custom, and when she had muttered, "From your Papists," she disappeared.

Southwell examined the page, noticing the word "copy" scrawled above the badly written paragraphs. He began to read:

Another warrant from their Lordships to Richard Topcliff and Richard Younge Esquires to examyn the said persons Christopher Baylles alias Evers a Seamenary Priest, John Bayles his brother a tayler, Henry Goorney haberdasher Antony Kaye and Jhon Coxed yoman from tyme to tyme, and if they see furder occasyon to comytte them or any of them unto such torture upon the wawle as is usuall for the better understanding of the trewthe of matters aginst her Maiestie and the Stayte. . . .

Southwell shuddered, picturing to himself the young priest's agony. True as steel, he would never inform. Probably Topcliffe had questioned him regarding the Jesuit Southwell's whereabouts.

There was a stir in the room. Melissa had returned to put some warm coals in the brazier. Presently she spoke, "That fiend Topcliffe could not pry a word out of him, though he hung for twenty-four hours by his hands. To every question he had one answer, 'I am a Catholic priest.' " She wiped her fingers on her apron and continued, "I was told to tell you that he will be tried."

"When?" demanded Southwell.

"Word will be brought. That is all that I can tell you," she replied and left the room.

How crabbed Melissa, a non-Catholic in the service of the devout Countess, was made aware of everything that happened to his recusant friends, Southwell did not know. And he was too wise to question her.

Some days later, she told him the place appointed for the trial, and the approximate hour, for she sensed that he would feel in duty bound to hear his former pupil's defense. Southwell went to the court, mingled with the crowd and managed to see and hear what he never forgot. Christopher was charged with having been ordained overseas and coming to England to exercise his office. Asked if he had anything to say for himself before judgment was pronounced, he responded in a young, flutelike voice that penetrated to the furthest corner of the room, "This only do I want to know, whether Saint Augustine, sent hither by Saint Gregory, was a traitor or not."

"He was not," came the answer.

"Why then do you condemn me to death as a traitor? I am sent hither by the same See; and for the same purpose he was. Nothing is charged against me that could not also be charged against the Saint."

"The act has since been made treason by law," explained the Judge.

Southwell, listening, thought, "Condemned as a traitor to his country because he is a priest. And because making a jerkin for a priest and sheltering him from the cold gave comfort to the enemy, Horner and Blake will also be hanged, no doubt."

On March the fourth, Melissa appeared with a small spray of white plum blossoms in her hand. She greeted Southwell, who, wearing a black velvet suit, the garb of a courtier, was about to make a call at Sackville House where Lady Margaret Sackville was ill.

"They have erected a scaffold on Fleet Street, at the foot of Fetter Lane, close to Sackville House," said Melissa. "As you leave the mansion after your call, put these white flowers in your hat. Plum blossoms for courage, they say."

Bewildered, he hesitated, but took the flowers she gave him.

"Your friend will be there. He wants your blessing. When he sees the white flowers in your hat, he will recognize you on the edge of the crowd. And when you raise your hand to remove them, you will really raise it in blessing. Papist doings that I don't condone. But you are both young," and Melissa departed, leaving a Jesuit dressed in black velvet holding a bouquet.

And so it was thanks to a dour serving woman that Southwell heard Father Christopher Bales' last words and gave him his blessing. Things happened quite as she had predicted, for when he left Sackville House he saw a scaffold on which hung a sign that read, "For Treason and aiding foreign enemies." A crowd had gathered, and from where he stood in the background he saw Christopher mount the scaffold, and heard his sweet, clear voice:

"Far be it from me to glory save in the Cross of Our Lord Jesus Christ," then saw him try to make the Sign of the Cross with his bound hands.

Suddenly the mob was silent, and Christopher's words came to Southwell over the heads of the crowd: "You have come to see a man dying, a common spectacle; and that man a priest, a common spectacle, too. But I wish that as you watch my body you could see into the inmost feeling of my heart . . . I ask pardon of you all and forgive you all. . . ."

Southwell's coat was twitched by an urchin beside him. "The posies in your hat, sir? It's too soon to go a-Maying."

"Thank you for reminding me," he said to the child. Then seeing the prisoner's eyes on him, he raised his hand, ostensibly to remove the delicate spray of bloom.

A smile played on the white face of the young priest. He began his final prayers, and with calm courage met his end.

"They're hanging a tailor in Smithfield," a passer-by remarked in Southwell's hearing.

"Yes," replied the man's companion, "one Nicholas Horner.

And there's another hanging in Gray's Inn Lane. A man named Blake."

"People grew tired of going to Tyburn," continued the first speaker. "So Old Top brought the show to town."

Chapter 22

By the autumn of 1591, Southwell needed a little rest from his London cares, so it was with a grateful heart that he received word from Father Garnet that he and the other Jesuits, along with some secular priests and a few lay Catholics, were expected at Baddesley Clinton for the semi-annual meeting at which the Jesuits would make General Confessions and renew their vows. He was thankful, too, that he could make the hundred-mile journey with his friend Father John Gerard, and discuss with him on the way the numerous matters on his mind.

On this journey into Warwickshire, Southwell told the younger Jesuit the change in his way of living. Anne Howard, anxious to be as near the Earl as possible, had moved to a house near the Tower. He had found quarters elsewhere, but, without Melissa to watch, he was in greater danger of being arrested when he stayed with the Cottons in Fleet Street or with his connections at Southampton House. Also, the thought was always with him that his presence endangered those who received him. And in addition to finding lodgings for himself, he had had to provide for priests who arrived from the Continent.

At Baddesley Clinton both priests threw themselves heart and soul into the spirit of the gathering, determined to draw closer to God and become more expert in directing the consciences of their Catholic friends. This last was a particularly difficult matter, for the questions put to those who sheltered priests, or members of a family who had heard Mass, were such that a Catholic might feel that he had to decide whether to tell a lie or to deliver a person over to torture and death. The solution reached was that *when a just cause is present*—when, for instance, a brute demands information to which he is not entitled and which might mean the slaying of the innocent—there is some kind of verbal misleading which is not sin.

Although Baddesley Clinton had been readied by "Little John" for the Jesuits' meeting, and although the Ladies Vaux were in residence there, served by a faithful Catholic staff, this gathering was larger than had been anticipated and some of those present realized the danger. Coming from many directions, some of them might have been secretly trailed by Topcliffe's men, and the mansion, hitherto deemed safe, might no longer be so.

There were eleven priests and several laymen, and when they had been together for several days and had had conferences with Father Garnet, the Superior, one of the men asked, "What would we do if the priest-hunters arrived?"

Southwell looked up and smiled. Nobody knew better than he that the hiding place on the roof would conceal only six men, and that it was difficult to reach; he knew, also, that it would require some time for that many grown men to let themselves down through the window seat or the trap door in the sacristy . . . they were not so small and light as little Frances Burrows. Nor was she here to lead the way.

Father Garnet exchanged glances with Southwell. He, too, knew the hiding places well. Finally, after a few seconds' pause, he answered, "Yes. It is perhaps unwise for all of us to

141

be here at one time. But this meeting is for God's glory. I shall be responsible until we have renewed our vows; then you will make your own decisions."

Accustomed to obedience, the Jesuits continued their conferences, made General Confessions and renewed their vows. Then, at the dinner table on October the 18th, Father Garnet announced, "I can no longer guarantee your safety." It was with great relief that he saw some of the priests and their guests mount their horses and ride off soon after dinner.

Two secular priests and several Jesuits remained. Among these were Southwell and Gerard and Father Oldcorne, whose home was Hinlip Hall, just eighteen miles away. Southwell knew that he had best put off his departure until the morning of the nineteenth, when he could get an early start and not be too many nights on the way back to London.

All were up very early, having given orders that their horses be saddled and everything in readiness for them to leave after Mass. At five o'clock Southwell, Gerard, Oldcorne, Father Stanney, and the Superior were in the Mass-chamber. Southwell had vested and was about to celebrate Mass, and Miss Anne Vaux, whose sister Mrs. Brooksby had not yet come down, was kneeling making her preparation.

Suddenly Southwell heard a terrific pounding at the locked and bolted front door. There were shouts and demands. Speedily he removed his vestments and stripped the altar. Miss Vaux rose, opened the shaft from the sacristy to the tunnel and called, "Father Southwell! Bring the chalice and patten and climb down. I will hand you the vestments and altar cloths."

Miss Vaux, quick as Frances herself would have been, almost pushed him down the shaft and shoved the missal and vestments into his arms. "Father Oldcorne," she ordered, "open the window seat and get through there quickly, and give Father Stanney a hand! Where is Father Gerard? Father Garnet, don't wait for him. Go first. He is big and might find it difficult to get through. I'll be here to help him squeeze in . . . Oh, I know what he is doing . . . turning the beds, so the ruffians won't find them warm and suspect that we have had guests."

Then, when Father Gerard had come, and she had seen him into the shaft and closed the opening, she flew off to tell a servant to go out the back way, unsaddle the horses and let them out to pasture. Then she went to the front door, where the pursuivants were insisting that they be admitted, and the servants were refusing.

"Open the door," said Miss Vaux. The servants complied.

"You are early callers," she said to the searchers as they rushed in. "My sister Mrs. Brooksby is not yet dressed to receive you. She will be here in a little while, if you care to wait." She went to a window, drew back the curtain, adjusted her tapestry frame and began to sort her colored skeins. "You will not be surprised that I am not at leisure to entertain you at the moment. As you see, I have undertaken some fancy work."

The leader looked at her in an angry fashion. "We shall entertain ourselves, Madam. We have cause to think that you have priests here, and we shall make a thorough search." He called his followers, and they went through the house, overturning furniture, opening closets, knocking walls, examining chimneys.

Miss Vaux stood quietly by her tapestry frame, then when it was light enough began to work quite as if she were in the house alone. After several hours, when every nook and corner had been searched, and "Little John's" entrances had not been discovered, the searchers began to tire, and the leader was not sorry when Miss Vaux said, "I have had breakfast prepared for you. When you have satisfied your appetites, I shall be glad to reward you for the pains of your search. We always pay Mr. Topcliffe's agents."

Somewhat baffled, the leader called off the search, and after the men had eaten and been paid, all took their departure.

Miss Vaux waited a while, then having sent for Mrs. Brooksby, who was timid and had a hiding place of her own, she bade her call their guests from the tunnel.

Up came the priests, weary and bedraggled, their hair mussed, their feet wet, for water had seeped into the tunnel from the moat.

Miss Vaux was already in the Mass-chamber. "Here, Father Southwell, hand me the altar cloths. I will get everything ready while you vest," she said, as Southwell and the others entered the room, Southwell with the cloths over his arm and the chalice in his hand, and Gerard bearing the missal. The altar prepared, she returned to her former place and knelt down to say her prayers before Mass.

Four hours had passed when Southwell began the delayed Mass, and nobody seeing his serene and happy expression would have thought there had been any interruption.

Chapter 23

After the October meeting at Baddesley Clinton, Southwell returned to London and stayed in a small house in Moorfields that "Little John" had prepared as a hiding place for the Jesuits. It was not far from Bishopsgate, where the Countess Anne was living.

It had been a painful season. Philip Howard was still in the Tower; his sister, Lady Margaret Sackville, had died; Southwell's cousin Margaret Copley Gage and her husband John Gage had been arrested and condemned to death because they had harbored priests, and it was only when they were in the cart at the scaffold, about to be hanged, that they were reprieved by the Queen because Lord Howard of Effingham had interceded for them. Headstrong Anthony Copley, Margaret's young brother, had returned to England from the Continent, where he had served in the Prince of Parma's army. He had spent some time as a prisoner in the Tower, and was forever the cause of anxiety to his family.

Southwell heard that the priest-hunter had threatened to have him hanged, and there seemed small reason to doubt that he would, for he was increasingly powerful. Was it possible that the Queen did not know the extent of the sufferings inflicted on her Catholic subjects by the tyrant?

At this point, the Queen issued a *Proclamation* in which the English missionary priests were described as "a multitude of dissolute young men who have, partly for lack of a living, partly for crimes committed, become fugitives, rebels and traitors. . . ." In the *Proclamation* was the statement that the young priests had been sent from the Seminaries to persuade Elizabeth's subjects "to renounce their natural allegiance."

When Southwell saw this horrible *Proclamation*, he decided to write an answer. Sir Francis Walsingham had died, the Queen and Lord Burghley were getting old, and it seemed that Sir Robert Cecil, Lord Burghley's cold and selfish son, and the tyrant Topcliffe were about to offer even worse indignities to the English Catholics.

Taking a printed copy of the *Proclamation* for reference, Southwell sat down in the Moorfields cottage, took paper and pen, and wrote the heading, "An Humble Supplication to Her

Majesty." Then he inscribed the lines of address to Elizabeth: "Most mighty and most merciful, most feared and best beloved Princess." He wrote at white heat, for he was determined that no thought of polished style or carefully weighed words should deflect from a straightforward account of the Catholics' loyalty and their persecution for their Faith. Surrounded by men who wanted her favor, it was barely possible that the Sovereign did not know what hideous things were done in her name. Not since his own kinsman Richard Shelley had attempted to do so in a petition in 1585 had Catholics dared present their case to the Queen. Shelley had been imprisoned and died without trial, and such might be his own lot but, with his Superior's permission, he was taking the chance.

Because the *Proclamation* accused Catholics of conspiracy, Southwell went into detail concerning the parts played by Sir Francis Walsingham, his forger Thomas Phelippes and Gilbert Gifford, the renegade, when they duped rash Anthony Babington and furthered plans for a plot involving the Queen of Scots.

Writing through the dark days of early winter, the usually gentle poet was so excited that he scarcely needed heat or light. For once, someone was putting in plain words the recusants' case, showing how the Government had used the weak and wicked as tools and had impoverished the strong. He took special exception to the *Proclamation's* saying that the recusants suffered no punishments for Religion; he asserted that they suffered all punishments for nothing else.

Determined that the Queen have a chance to know the manner of Topcliffe's tortures, Southwell did not mince words: "Some are hanged by their hands, eight or nine or twelve hours together, till not only their wits but even their senses fail them; and when the soul, weary of so painful a harbor, is ready to depart, they apply cruel comforts, and revive us only to martyr us with more deaths; for, soon again, they hang us in the same manner, trying our ears with such questions which either we cannot, because we know not, or, without damning our souls, we may not, satisfy. . . . Some have been watched and kept from sleep till they are past the use of reason, then examined upon that advantage, when they could scarcely give an account of their own names. . . ."

Having declared Catholics loyal Englishmen, he continued, "We will rather yield our breasts to be broached by our Country's swords than use our swords to shed our Country's blood." He went on to explain why Catholics, persecuted for their religion, could not go to the services of the Church of England, the Queen's church: "For as there is no way so well known or usual to distinguish any religion from another as the external rites and sacraments peculiar to every one, so none can so effectually deny his own religion as by making open profession of a contrary Faith, by his assistance and presence at the solemnities and services proper unto it." Thorough to the end, he named the fines that recusants paid for not going to the Queen's church, and told how all the goods and two thirds of the lands of the wealthy were confiscated, and the cattle and bedding that belonged to the poor.

Southwell, with characteristic frankness, explained to his sovereign that this *Humble Supplication* was not being presented in person because of the fate of the previous petitioner, and that it was being broadcast to the multitude in the hope that, "among so many as shall peruse this short and true relation of our troubles, God will touch some merciful heart to let your Highness understand the extremity of them."

Straightway, when Southwell had finished, scriveners went to work and copied the letter. It was safer to entrust it to faithful Catholic friends to copy than to risk printing it even on a private press. When many copies had been made, they were distributed in the proper places.

Since few could write as well as Southwell did, and since already the literary set in London knew and admired his English style, it would be known that he was the author of *An Humble Supplication*. One of the first to marvel at the work was Richard Topcliffe, "Her Majesty's Servant." He recognized his favorite torment for recusants, and right then and there swore that if "that infamous traitor and Jesuit Robert Southwell" could be found by his searchers, he would himself see to it that he had firsthand experience of what he so skillfully described.

Chapter 24

In the long gallery at Warblington, two auburn heads were bent over a manuscript. One was a curly head and its ringlets glowed like red gold in the sun that streamed through the broad windows.

"Robin!" exclaimed Mary earnestly. "Will you never learn to spell? How can I copy a poem of yours when you write 'Heaven' in one verse and 'Hevenly' in the next?" She shook her head and pushed toward her brother the page from which she had been copying one of his poems for her commonplace book.

Southwell looked up from a dedication that he was writing to which he had just signed the initials *R.S.* He smiled at his sister. "You should see Will Shakespeare's spelling. He is a youth who is often with our cousin Wriothesley at Southampton House. He is gifted, I think, but he spells much as I do."

"Speaking seriously as is my custom," came an interruption from a young man sitting in the window seat, "speaking very seriously, I do declare correct spelling and not rhyming to be the present problem in England. The crying need is for someone to put order into our spelling and our lives." He flourished a manuscript. "Now take this poem over which I wrinkle my fair brow. The title is magnificent, 'A Fig for Fortune,' and—"

"Your title, Anthony?" asked Mary, laughing.

"Do not interrupt me," warned Anthony Copley, leaning over and pulling a curl. "Latin and Italian are civilized languages. I can spell Italian. But if you want to see the Queen's English butchered, get hold of Topcliffe's instructions to his searchers . . . or better still, their replies."

Mary shuddered.

Southwell questioned quickly, "Tony, have you seen searchers recently?"

Anthony Copley rose, walked over to his cousin, put his long thin fingers around his neck, and replied affectionately, "Guess, I shall not tell you! The Queen might send for me and chop off my head. I do not know why she let me out of the Tower. Perhaps she wants me for a favorite. But I detest wrinkles!"

Southwell and Mary exchanged glances.

"Careful, Tony, careful," murmured Mary.

"Careful, Mary, careful," retorted Anthony. "Yes, I know that you think you can win your way with any London warder, get into prison by smiling at the jailer, but. . . ."

"But," argued Mary, "the warders never see me smile." She shoved the manuscript away, rose, flung her shawl over her head, hunched her shoulders, screwed her eyelids until the cornflower blue beneath was hidden, shuffled over to Anthony and muttered, "Let a poor old soul in to see her young 'un. What did you say?" She cupped her ear with her hand. "What did you say?" she repeated. "Speak louder. No, no, talk so I

149

can hear ye." She stood on tiptoe and brushed Anthony's forehead with her lips, and continued, "No warders have the patience to resist me. They all get rid of me by letting me pass."

Southwell laughed aloud. "Yes, Tony, I have met that old woman in Fleet Jail, in Aunt Katherine's cell."

"So have I," agreed Margaret Copley Gage, coming in at that moment. She wore riding clothes. Her cheeks were pink and her gray eyes danced.

"Enter the Missing Martyr. Straight from the scaffold," announced Anthony with a deep bow to his older sister. "Robbed of her crown by an Admiral, no less."

Southwell rose to greet Margaret, and as he began to gather up his papers, she dropped to her knees for his blessing. He gave it gravely.

"How I dislike pillions!" she exclaimed, rising and smoothing her skirt. "John would not leave me at Roughey, and wouldn't let me ride alone, so I had to ride pillion! Did you know that the searchers had been at Roughey?"

"I suspected so," replied Southwell, "for Anthony, who rode down yesterday, was just now marveling at their wondrous spelling. He did not mention the search."

"It was not necessary," boasted Anthony. "I sent the spies in the wrong direction with the blessing of Lord Howard of Effingham. Margaret, what rhymes with 'fig' except 'big?' "

"Gig, rig, dig, pig," said Margaret, taking a chair.

"Ah . . . the country lass . . . dig, pig . . . there is a suggestion of the farm in your speech, sweet sister. I've invented a farm-sounding term myself, 'to craven-cockadoodle it.' But let's be elegant for a change. To the virginal, Lady! Mary, fetch your lute! Robert, stow away your written words and sing!" Anthony went to a rack and selected some sheets of music written by William Byrd, and commanded, "A madrigal first, if you please."

150

In a trice the cousins were making music, and the long gallery was gay with song:

> Whyle the Sunne with his beames hot,
> Scorched the fruits in vale and mountain:
> Philon the shepherd late forgot,
> sitting beside a Christall fountaine,
> sitting beside a Christall fountaine, in
> shadow of a green Oke tree,
> upon his pipe this song played he. . . .

Chapter 25

The snow drops had been in bloom when Southwell arrived in Sussex. When these had disappeared, the plum trees had put out white blossoms. "Plum flowers for courage," he remembered Melissa's saying; perhaps she thought them brave to bloom so early. Then the daffodils had come. Now it was late spring, with hawthorn hedges snowy white by the roadsides and every dell full of yellow primroses. And Anthony Copley was accompanying him part way on his journey back to London.

"Let's make a detour and see the Forest," suggested Anthony, turning his mount into a side road.

Southwell hesitated an instant. But since his Superior had urged him not to hasten his return, he consented and followed. They ambled along, enjoying the warmth of the sun and the fragrance of clover, and keeping silence save when one or the other commented on a bird.

After a while they saw what seemed a veil of green ahead, and presently they were under a canopy of new leaves and surrounded by gray tree trunks. Their horses' hoofs made no sound on the soft road, and the stillness about them was such that they felt themselves in a mirage, caught up into an unreal world.

"Strong and quiet and undisturbed by time," said Southwell, looking at the trees. "They always remind me of the trees that Saint Bernard called his professors. I delight in Saint Bernard's writings, you know."

"Saints and professors!" taunted Anthony. "But I was indulging my fancy also, with a poet and two angels in verdant vesture. You remember Dante's description in *The Divine Comedy* of the angels' raiment:

Verdi, come fogliette pur mo nate,

How would you translate that Italian line, Robert?"

"Green, like little new-born leaves," suggested Southwell.

"Green, as tender leaflets born today," offered Anthony. "Is yours better than mine?"

"Neither is as musical as Dante's," answered Southwell. "And here you and I are, as always, dealing with words. Yet, words are for the greater glory of God . . . words express God's truth. . . ."

" 'In the beginning was the Word, and the Word was with God, and the Word was God,' " quoted Anthony from Saint John's Gospel. "Even Our Lord is described as 'the Word.' "

Southwell, without speaking, reined in his horse. Anthony did the same. They sat in silence until the latter said, "Robert, you have always been articulate; you have used words easily; you have spoken and written for yourself and others." His voice trembled. "I have something to tell you. I learned from the searchers at Havant the other day that Topcliffe has copies of your *Supplication*. He lent one to Sir Francis Bacon, who sent it to his brother Anthony. Topcliffe has vowed you shall hang."

Southwell smiled serenely. "I suppose so."

"But I am going to London with you to protect you . . . I—" Anthony broke off.

"You are going back to help Edward and John protect Mary and Margaret, Tony. I shall be happier if I know that you are with them . . . for their sake and yours."

Anthony looked into Robert's eyes a moment. "You have always understood me. You know that I am wild by nature; you knew that when I was in Rome. You are sure that I would fall in with the wrong crowd in London, aren't you?"

Southwell's expression was very gentle when he replied, "Sussex is the place for you, Tony."

Without another word, Anthony dismounted and knelt on the ground. "You are holy, Robin. Bless me."

Southwell raised his hand in blessing, and then said, "We part here probably never to meet on earth again. Take care of my blue-eyed Mary." Then as Anthony stood beside him, he leaned over and they clasped hands.

Anthony mounted, waved, and was off by the road they had come.

Southwell, deep in thought, jogged along toward the house at which he would dine. Certainly Anthony was better off in Sussex than he would be with the thoughtless youths in London. His mind turned to another Anthony . . . Anthony Babington and the Bellamy family of Harrow-on-the-Hill, who had suffered so much because of their acquaintance with him. This morning, before they had set out, word had reached them that Topcliffe, who had arrested Richard Bellamy's oldest daughter Anne in January for religion, and had held her in the Gatehouse Prison, was now demanding that her father consent to her marriage with his servant Nicholas Jones, and that he bestow on her his fine manor of Preston as a dower. Poor girl! In Topcliffe's power, she would be tormented with questions about Catholics who were lodging in that neighborhood, at Southampton House and Gray's Inn. There were always Catholic law students at the latter. He prayed that Anne might have the courage not to inform.

Southwell rode on over the Downs. They were golden in the afternoon light, and the clear sky above was blue. It was rare to see the heavens above England so blue . . . yet England was Our Lady's Dower and blue her color.

All went well on his journey back to the city. On the way he visited recusant friends. He said Mass early and paused afterward to read his office, thanking God, as he always did, for the beauty of the psalms. It was evening when he reached London Bridge. He looked up at the Gatehouse and lifted his hat reverently. Some of the heads on the spikes there now had belonged to his martyrs.

"Queen of Martyrs, pray for me," he entreated. Then he mingled with the crowd on the bridge. He began to think of his father and brothers who might be in the city that very moment. He had written to his father but had not seen him since his return to England, and the fact that he had not been able to win him back to the Church was a sorrow. But God was merciful. Perhaps what had not been accomplished by his letter would be brought to pass by his death. " 'Greater love than this no man hath, that a man lay down his life for his friends,' " he thought, and then added to himself: "One's dearest friends are in one's family. I must trust. I may never know while I live. But surely the Holy Spirit will enlighten my father and he will receive the Sacraments." He smiled. "Our Lady will listen to my blue-eyed Mary. Mary and not I will see Father reconciled to the Church."

Chapter 26

There had been a summer shower, but as Southwell and young Thomas Bellamy rode up the drive at Uxendon, the morning sun came out. The wet gray slates of the roof of the manor house gleamed, and rain drops glistened on the trellised roses. The lawn in front of the mansion was green, and bright flowers bloomed in the gardens. Southwell, who had ridden from murky London with Thomas, took a deep breath and thought how pleasant it was to be in the country again. This was Sunday. He would say Mass, spend the day and night and then ride on to join Father Garnet in Warwickshire. On Monday Father Richard Blount would meet him, so he would have a companion for the journey.

A groom came to take the horses, and Mrs. Bellamy, the mistress of the house, followed by her daughters Mary and Audrey, greeted Southwell at the open door. After kissing Tom she turned to the groom, saying, "When the horses are cared for, bring all the stablemen in for Mass. The gardeners are already in preparing for confession."

As Southwell mounted the steps, she said, "Your messenger brought word that Tom had asked you to come, Father. My daughter Anne is in great trouble, as you know, and is lodged by Mr. Topcliffe in Holborn. My husband is away from home. Our household is Catholic, and it has been a sorrow to us not to have Mass and the Sacraments."

Southwell answered, "Your son called on me yesterday and said that his sister begged me to stop with you the first night of my journey from London. So we arranged for me to arrive in time to celebrate Mass."

Mrs. Bellamy looked up suddenly. She seemed startled, bewildered. "His sister?" she began. "Tom. . . ." she turned to question her son, but he had disappeared into the house. "Father Southwell," she continued, "before you begin to hear confessions or to vest, let me show you the hiding place. No priest has ever been caught here at Uxendon, although many priests, including Father Campion and Father Persons, have stayed here. And, of course, we have frequently had searchers."

She walked a little ahead and he followed her up six steps of the stairway to where it turned at the first landing. There she paused, stooped, touched a spring and lifted several boards by means of a concealed hinge. Then she removed a bundle of horsehair, slid over a trap door that ran in grooves, and stood aside for him to peer into a room beneath. A ladder led down to the floor, and the room, about ten feet square and nine feet high, was furnished with a cot and chair, a table with candles and a basin and ewer.

"You will see, Father, that the fireplace is a sham. The brick chimney is, in fact, a shaft placed against the main chimney; it admits air and light from above, and there is a ladder enclosed by which one can reach the roof. The floor is directly on the ground, which was scooped out. The room has no connection with the cellars. The tiny circles that you will see over the cot are the ends of tubes that convey sound through the wall from the hall and adjoining rooms. They are cleverly concealed outside, but a person in this room can hear everything said in the hall. There are false walls there, well lined, so that a searcher's sword or stick never strikes a hollow place. The whole is built on the principal that it is unsafe to let any wall give forth a hollow sound; such walls are always broken into. The chests for vestments in the Mass-chamber are arranged on the same principle. They are set at floor level, behind sliding panels, and they fill the hollowed walls completely."

Southwell, looking down into the room, saw that his belongings had already been placed there and realized that it was to be his bedchamber. "Father Campion slept here?" he asked, as Mrs. Bellamy and he backed down a few steps and closed the boards on the landing.

"Yes. In my mother-in-law's day. Properly speaking, this is not a priest's-hole, but rather an ancient hiding place. This portion of the house dates back to Richard II's time. The fact of the room's existence has been kept secret through several generations. Each member of the family knows the spot, but none but the most trusted of our serving people. This way to the Mass-chamber, Father," she added, ascending the stairs and preceding him along a narrow corridor that opened on a long gallery immediately above the front door.

When they entered the gallery, Southwell saw that an altar had been prepared, and a confessional improvised with a screen. Audrey and Mary and their brothers were kneeling near the altar, and toward the end of the room were the farmers and serving people, all solemnly and reverently making ready for confession.

Mrs. Bellamy motioned him to a chair behind the screen, made her confession, and was followed by her family and the others. It was all so quiet and matter of fact, the devotion of all was so evident, that when he began to vest for Mass Southwell thought of Campion's letter to Rome about the faith of the persecuted English, and of his own letter to the Father General describing the recusants' eagerness for Holy Communion.

He approached the altar, and recited the *Judica me* and the

157

Confiteor. There was not a sound from outside save the soft mourning of doves, and inside nothing distracted him from adoration during the Canon or when he was giving Holy Communion to the courageous congregation.

"Lord, it is good for us to be here," he kept thinking, and added to himself: "It was for this that I crossed the Channel and the Alps, for this that I spent my youth in Rome."

Mass finished, the altar was stripped, and the missal and vestments were stowed immediately in the secret chests and the sliding panels closed. Then all knelt in thanksgiving until, one by one, different persons slipped away to the pantry or kitchen or their household occupations.

The peace of the morning lingered through the day. Southwell walked up and down in the garden reading his breviary, and then seeing that there would be no further call for him, he picked up a stout furze stick and started for a stroll. At that season, the light would last well into the evening, and it was a long while since he had seen a sunset in the country. So thinking, he took a wooded path that led from the manor of Uxendon to nearby Harrow-on-the-Hill.

He swung along through the glades and clearings. The earth was moist and fragrant. Birds twittered in the copses, and as he climbed toward his destination, he noticed bits of old rock wall with flower-filled crannies.

Presently the light ahead seemed brighter, then in a second he was out of the woodland and standing on the crest of a hill. He looked up to the wide expanse of evening sky, down over the tree tops of Saint John's Wood and the hedge-bound gardens that marked the roads through Middlesex, and away to the spires of London clustered on the horizon. Gold-flecked clouds threw ever deepening blue shadows on the landscape, and the whole scene was one of peace.

He lingered a while, looked at distant London and turned and walked swiftly back to Uxendon.

It was supper time when he arrived. After supper and night prayers, the younger members of the family knelt for his blessing, took their candles and went off to their rooms. But Mrs. Bellamy lingered, saying, "Father Southwell, I questioned Audrey and Mary; then I questioned Tom. The message requesting you to come reached Tom not from his sisters here but. . . ."

"From Anne?" he asked, and continued, "I suspected that when you told me that a messenger had come from me. I sent no messenger."

"This is Topcliffe's doing!" she exclaimed. "You must be away before dawn, Father. Do not wait for Father Blount. Tonight, stay in the priest's room, no matter what happens. A servant is posted to give warning should the searchers arrive during the night. I have had a fire built against the chill, and shall doze by it for a while." She knelt at the foot of the stairs. He blessed her, thanked her, and bade her good night.

The entrance to the hiding place had been opened, so Southwell dropped down onto the ladder, pulled-to the hinged boards, stuffed the bundle of horsehair between them and the sliding trap door, closed this, then climbed down to the floor. Preparing for the night, he remembered experiences with searchers and decided to remain fully clothed, as he had on previous occasions.

He had scarcely fallen asleep when he was awakened by the clatter of horses' hoofs outside, the riders' shouts, banging on doors and windows, demands for entrance.

"The pursuivants are here," came a warning through one of the tubes above his cot. He could not tell whether the voice was Audrey's or Mary's. It continued, "Keep still. Do not make a sound. A servant is delaying them a moment. Mother will meet them."

Suddenly the voices came from inside the hall. Swords clanked. Searchers swore and shouted. The odor of wax from many candles that had been lighted reached his nostrils. Then one sharp, shrill voice above the turmoil: "I am here to arrest Cotton, the Jesuit."

"I know no Cotton," replied a woman's voice calmly. "Have you a warrant?"

"For his arrest. And yours, for harboring a priest," came the rough answer.

Southwell listened.

"You are at liberty to search," said the woman.

"I do not need to search. Read these directions in your own daughter's handwriting. She gives the exact location of the priest's hole. She was promised that if she contrived the arrest of the Jesuit Robert Southwell, no harm would come to her family. The fool! She sent your stupid son to fetch him. My man Nicholas Jones watched, and word was brought to me at the Court at Greenwich, and. . . ."

Southwell made the Sign of the Cross, mounted the ladder, opened the trap door and the hinged boards quietly and stood a second looking down from the dark stairs to the brilliantly lighted hall. Then noiselessly he replaced the covering of the priest's hole, hoping that it might be forgotten. Not a board creaked as he descended the stairs.

Standing perfectly still for an instant at the foot of the stairs, he was not observed by the haranguing tyrant Topcliffe or his crew of ruffians. Then the leader, thin, gray-haired, with gimlet eyes, spied him and shouted, "Who are you?"

"A gentleman," replied Southwell serenely. He remembered where he had seen those peering eyes: in the passage near Gray's Inn Road when he was about to call on Christopher Bales.

"A gentleman!" shrieked Topcliffe. "You mean a priest and a traitor!"

160

"If you seek blood, you shall have mine," said Southwell, "but remember, God is just in His judgments."

Topcliffe lunged at Southwell with his rapier. The local magistrate, who had accompanied the pursuivants, and another bystander fended him off. It would not do to let "Her Majesty's Servant" murder his prey.

"Fitzherbert! Get you off to Greenwich and inform the Queen of the capture!" commanded Topcliffe. He shouted to others of the company, "Here! Some of you one-time Papists swear who he is and that you've been to his Masses."

Several swore as ordered.

"Bind the traitor and throw him into the cart. And get along with you. I'll meet you at my house at Westminster. No jail for this traitor yet; this is a personal matter." Topcliffe's voice had become like an angry animal's roar.

Southwell, standing still and being bound with ropes, looked up at Audrey and Mary, who were crouched on the stair. "God bless you," he said, his tone sweet and clear. "And think kindly of your sister. Already she has suffered more than I."

Chapter 27

Westminster Abbey towered above Richard Topcliffe's dwelling and the nearby Gatehouse Prison. There was very little light in the room in which the grizzled giant had been questioning Southwell. The priest, his auburn hair mussed and his white face streaked with dirt from the cart in which he had been brought from Uxendon to Topcliffe's house, was on a stool, his arms bound. He had steadfastly refused to give any information save what was already known, his name and the fact that he was a Jesuit priest. His lips were set and his hands clenched and his manner determined, yet there was a flicker of amusement in his expression now and then while he watched "Her Majesty's Servant" at a table laboriously composing a letter to the Queen.

"Here, you Jones!" shouted Topcliffe to Nicholas Jones, his servant, "bring me another candle. There's not enough light in this den to see by."

Jones, a slimy-looking man, hastened over with several candles and lighted them. Then Topcliffe continued his letter. Could Southwell have seen the spelling, he would have agreed with Anthony Copley that it was even worse than Will Shakespeare's. The letter ran:

Most graceoos Sovereigne, havinge fr. Robert Southwell (to my knowledge) *the* Jhezewt in my stronge chamber in Westmi*nster* churche yearde. I have mayde assewred fo startinge, or hortinge of himself. By puttinge upon his armes a *pair* of hande gyeves: ct There ct so can keepe hym eather from vewe, or Conferrence with any, But Nicolas *the* underkeep*er* of the Gayt howse ct my Boye Nicholas beinge the man *that* caused me to tayke hym, by settinge of hym into my hands, *ten* myles from him.

I have presewmed (after my lytell sliepe) to runne over this Ex-*a*minatio*n* incloassed, faythfully tayken, ct of him fowlye ct suspycioosly answered, ct sumwhat knowinge the Natewre ct doinges of the man, May it please yo*ur* maj*e*sty to see my simple opynyon. Constreigned in dewty to utter it.

Upon this present taykynge of hym, It is good foorthewith to inforce him to answer trewlye, ct dyrectly, ct so to proove his answers trewe in hast, To the Ende, *that* such as bee deeply conserned in his treacherees have no time to start, or mayke shyfte.

To use any meanes in common presons eather to stande upon or ageinst the wawle (which above all thinges exceds ct horteth not) will gyve warninge. But if *your* high*ness* pleasor be to knowe anythinge in this hartte, To stande against the wawle, His feett standinge upon the grownde, ct his hands But as highe as he can reatche ageinst *the* wawle, lyke a Tryck at Trenshemoare will inforce to tell all, ct the trewthe prooved by *the* Sequelle.

The answer of him to *the* Questyon of *the* Countesse of Arundell, ct that of father Parsons, discipherethe him. . . .

Southwell, sitting on the stool, with the gyves or shackles on his arms, easily imagined what the priest-hunter was writing, and his surmise was confirmed when Nicholas Jones was again called and the letter read aloud to him.

"You hear that?" demanded Topcliffe, waving the letter in front of the Jesuit. "We'll let you see how it *feels* to hang against the wall. Poet! Writer! *Supplication to Her Majesty* indeed! You will soon be telling everything you know about the Earl of Arundel and his offspring and the Countess, and that Jesuit Persons and the Pope and all your papistical knavery and sedition! You'll be telling who schemed with you in Sussex and Hampshire, in Fleet Street, aye, and at Southampton House, too, with all your grand kin. Here, Jones! Hand me my Seal. Now, away with you to Greenwich with this letter to the Queen."

But the priest was not listening. His hour was at hand. He must pray for courage. Always when meditating on the sufferings of Christ, he had understood what it must have meant to know about them before they came to pass. He wondered if the torture that he was about to undergo would be as dreadful as he had imagined it when Christopher Bales and others had endured it.

Very soon, he knew. It was worse, far worse than anything he had thought possible. Rough men seized him, and swung

163

him by the cruel gyves from the wall. Finding that his toes touched the floor, they tied his legs up to his waist. Again and again he would faint with pain, and would be revived and questioned.

"What was the color of the horse you rode that day?" he was asked. "Who were your companions?" Innumerable questions were put to him in the hope that he would betray recusants into Topcliffe's hands. But he kept resolute silence, for did they know the color of the horse, they might discover where it was stabled or the owner's name. Sometimes he would pray aloud, begging God's help and calling out, "My Lord and my God!"

After a day or two of such torture in Topcliffe's strong-chamber, Southwell was conveyed to the Gatehouse Prison, and thrown in with the dirty vagrants who swarmed there. The tortures were renewed, and he was purposefully deprived of sleep. Ten times he underwent the hanging. Sometimes he threw up blood. Sir Robert Cecil, Lord Burghley's son, cruel Justice Richard Young and others came to question him. Sir Robert Cecil, who saw him suspended, remarked on his being as dumb as a tree trunk, not uttering a word. Yet, when anyone save Topcliffe had occasion to talk with him when he was not being interrogated, his gentleness and courtesy made a profound impression. With Topcliffe he maintained perfect silence, knowing himself helpless with a heart so hardened.

Finally, after several weeks of useless questioning, the young priest was simply left to suffer the effects of what he had been through. Neglected, filthy, almost entirely helpless, he lay in prison. He wondered, perhaps, if he ever would be tried and condemned. Surely death by hanging on the gallows would be infinitely easier to endure than the pain of torture, the filth and stench of the Gatehouse Jail.

And in truth, although he did not know it at the time, he had been through the worst. From now on he would accept the

164

hardships and not dread his weakness, for with God's help he had proven himself brave. In his boyhood, he had written in his book of devotions, "Since in very truth God gave His life for thee, more precious than that of all the angels in Heaven, what great matter dost thou think it to offer thy life for His cause and love?"

Chapter 28

Without attempting to lift his head, Southwell half-opened his eyes. Nothing different greeted them, for he saw the damp prison wall against which his pallet was placed, his wrinkled and soiled garments, and a verminous bit of blanket which had been thrown over his feet. Yet, there had been a change of some kind. It seemed to be in his aching wrists; it was as if they were being tenderly stroked by gentle hands. With difficulty, he turned his head to one side and saw the fringe of a black shawl. Someone was sitting beside his pallet. He closed his eyes again, then opened them a little wider and saw a tiny old woman crouched by his side. God bless her, he prayed, thinking that one of the paupers who were his fellow prisoners had taken pity on him.

He felt soothed by the stroking, comforted by the presence of another human being. Again he closed his eyes, too weak and weary to try to speak. He may have dozed a minute, then suddenly he was wide awake. He not only felt but also saw the hands that were touching his thin wrists. And they were soft, white, beautiful young hands; they were Mary's hands, which he had watched so often at Warblington when she was at the virginal or sat opposite him copying manuscripts.

"Robin, are you awake?" came a whisper.

"Yes, awake . . . fully awake. Have you been here long? Mary, you must not stay. The prison is filthy, full of loathesome things, vermin and rats. And there are diseased people."

"I cannot stay long, Robin. But let's speak together for a minute. I wanted you to know that you kept perfect silence . . . all London is talking about your refusal to tell the name of a single recusant. Sir Robert Cecil has spread the news of your bravery."

"God gave me the grace to be silent," murmured Southwell. "Mary, the pain of the torture is far, far worse than anyone can dream. We must not wonder that some lose courage."

"I have been with the Countess of Arundel, Robin. She says that you prepared yourself by using the remedy that you taught her: to expect the worst and beg God's help in bearing it."

"Yes, for us Catholics it is better to face matters than to buoy ourselves with false hope that the torture may be less than we think. It is more painful than the most vivid imagination could picture. But I am so weak physically now that I would faint immediately were I hanged by the wrists again, so I no longer dread that a denial of the Faith might be extorted from me. You know how I feared my possible weakness. Our family—"

"Our family," Mary interrupted, "has not always been true to the Faith. But Robin, I have great news for you about Father."

Southwell, startled, almost succeeded in raising his shoulders. "Father? Has he. . . ."

"Lie back, Robert. No, he has not returned to the Church. But he has been brave. He petitioned the Queen that, if you were deserving of death according to the law, you should suffer it; if not, that she should accord you a gentleman's treatment, even though you are a Jesuit, and permit him to pay for your support. Robin, it hurts Father's pride to have his son with paupers, neglected in a common jail."

"Nevertheless, he found it hard to make the request of Her Majesty. God bless him."

"Her Majesty is old," said Mary. "But she and Lord Burghley both know that our mother was her friend in girlhood. Uncle Thomas Copley did not let them forget the fact that the acquaintance lasted forty years."

Southwell smiled wanly. "Uncle Thomas! He used influence artfully. It is not the Queen who must be moved, however, but Her Majesty's Servant, Richard Topcliffe. Mary, you must obey me now. Leave immediately."

"Yes, Robert." She leaned over so that he could look into her blue eyes. "Do not try to lift your hand, but bless me. Do you remember that Anthony once said that I could pass the guards at the Tower? The Countess Anne and I are making plans. What will you want there except clean clothing and fresh linen?"

"My breviary. And my copy of Saint Bernard's writings. Topcliffe will never let me have pen and paper. He knows how to punish a poet. God bless you, Mary. Hurry. Even you might be caught here."

She was gone, gathered into the prison shadows, a black-clad, decrepit pauper.

Meanwhile, an order of the Privy Council was being dated July 25, 1592, and directed to the Lieutenant of the Tower of London:

To receive into your custody and charge the person of Robert Southwell a priest whom Mr. Topcliffe shall deliver unto you to be kept close prisoner so as no person be allowed to have access unto him but such an one as Mr. Topcliffe shall appoint to remain with him as his keeper. Herein we are to require you to take that order for the safe keeping and close restraining of the said Southwell as appertaineth, being a most lewd and dangerous person. . . .

Chapter 29

The Council's order to Sir Michael Blount, Lieutenant of the Tower, was so well obeyed that there is no record of any Catholic's ever seeing Southwell during the period of almost three years that he was confined there. There is a story to the effect that two ladies, perhaps Mary Southwell Banister and Margaret Copley Gage, gained admission to the Tower precincts, and seeing him in a window, received his blessing from a distance. From our knowledge that his prison was close to the Cradle Tower from which Father John Gerard later escaped to the Thames, it is surmised that he had a room in the Lanthorn Tower . . . the old Tower, later ruined by fire. This was the location of Philip Howard's former prison. He and Southwell were entirely separated, for he was either in Beauchamp or in another part of the Lanthorn. The Earl and his chaplain the poet did not see each other, although the Earl's dog once followed Sir Michael Blount to Southwell's room, and when he returned to his master, Philip said that he loved him the better for it.

For years, Countess Anne had been trying to establish communication with her husband, and although she had never found means to give him a glimpse of his little son, she had discovered a way to send an occasional message. She may have made use of this channel to forward to Southwell his copy of Saint Bernard's writings. And Father Garnet sent him his breviary. But he was denied pen and paper, and apparently made no effort to communicate with the outside world. Even Father Garnet, his Superior, who was familiar with secret agents, could only report in his letters to the Father General that Southwell was so closely confined that they scarcely knew whether he was living or dead.

Sir Robert Cecil questioned him. He was determined that the Jesuit should not appear a hero when the time for his trial came. Just as Campion had been falsely accused of being a dangerous enemy, guilty of plotting, so Southwell's holding that equivocation was at times permissible would be played up as a menace to the Government. Sir Robert Cecil wished to trap him into discussing this theory of equivocation and ensnaring himself.

A frequent caller was Sir Michael Blount, who although he disliked Philip Howard intensely, was attracted to the gentle Southwell.

It seems probable that Southwell, who had once been anxious to lead the quiet life of a Carthusian monk, accepted the fact that God was giving him a season of seclusion in which to prepare for death. For years he had written what was in his heart to say. His letters of advice to the recusants, his pleading with the Queen for their rights, his translations of works of devotion and his poems, had been circulated in manuscript and printed. And he was credited with having influenced Shakespeare and others of his circle to use their talents for good. He knew that what he had recorded in words would outlive his bodily heart and tongue; he could rest in the thought that his apostolic work of that nature was done. Now he had only to accept what he was called on to endure and pray for courage for himself and others.

Right there in the Tower were others who were in need of his prayers. Sir Michael Blount sent a report to the Council that may be read today in *The Calendar of State Papers* of Great Britain for the year 1594.

List of Prisoners in the Tower, under the custody of Sir Mich. Blount, lieutenant;
Viz: Philip Howard late Earl of Arundel
  Roger Lopez, Doctor of Physic
  Stephen Ferrera de Garma, Manuel Louis Tonoco
and John Ardent, all of whom are condemned.

There are also confined there:
  Jas. Fitzgerald, son of the late Earl of Desmond
  Edm. Neville, Confederate with Parry to kill the Queen
  Sir Nick Clifford
  Peter Wentworth, committed from the Parliament
  Hen. Duffield, a sea captain, committed from
    the Lord Admiral

  Robert Southwell, alias Cotton, a Jesuit and
    infamous traitor
  Henry Walpole, a Jesuit lately come over to do
    mischief
  John Ingram, a Jesuit or priest
  Robt Humberton & Robt. Lingham, recusants
  Gilbert Laton, sent from Rochelle to kill the
    Queen, a man of great importance
  John Amias an Irishman who came over
    under pretence of killing Antonio Perez

  There are also divers priests and other dangerous
  persons in the Marshalsea, Gatehouse and other prisons,
  has not yet had full certification of them.
      April 14, 1594.

A practice in which the Government indulged was that of telling the Catholic prisoners that their fellow priests had conformed under torment and had given up their religion. The despicable Richard Young had tried to convince the Jesuit John Gerard, who was a prisoner in the Clink, that Southwell was ready to conform! Doubtless Southwell himself was told of the hideous sufferings and occasional apparent yieldings of Father Henry Walpole, then a prisoner in the nearby Salt Tower. Perhaps it was falsely hinted to him that John Ingram, who had been his student at the English College in Rome, had weakened. But, experienced in the trickery of his persecutors, he was too wise to believe such tales. There was but one way to peace, and that was to pray that all would be faithful and brave, and leave all in God's care.

Southwell could not celebrate Mass or approach the Sacraments. But he had taught his penitents to choose an hour daily during which they said their Mass prayers privately and made a Spiritual Communion; in spirit, they were thus united with all the Masses being offered. He meditated, of course, thankful for his knowledge of the methods taught by Ignatius of Loyola. And when there were long, dark, lonely hours to get through, he said the fifteen mysteries of the Rosary, counting the Hail Marys on his fingers. Some kind of a record he kept for himself, for when the breviary that had been smuggled in to him was examined later, it was found to have been systematically pricked. On one page the word "Jesus" was scratched with a pin, on another, "My God and my All."

Father Garnet, the Superior, trusted this fine brave priest whom he knew so well, and although he could not see him or get word from him, he wrote the Father General later that it seemed that God had given him strengthening such as one gets in a novitiate, and that he had received such courage and vigor during his imprisonment that, at the time of his trial, his tranquillity and serenity amazed unbelievers. Perhaps, after all, these hidden years in the Tower of London, these Carthusian years granted to a Jesuit, were among the most fruitful of Southwell's life.

For some reason, Southwell was not tortured in the Tower as Campion had been or as Henry Walpole then was. Perhaps he had been so weakened at the Gatehouse Prison that the Council thought that he would die under torture. There is a faint possibility that, his high connections being known, his family's friendships with Lord Admiral Howard, the Wriothesleys, Southwells and others, the Council hesitated to order further torture. However, it is more probable that his persecutors were merely biding their time. Sir Robert Cecil, at least, seems to have guessed that Southwell would be a willing martyr. Finally, when two years had passed and Southwell suggested that he be tried, the dapper Secretary replied that if he were so anxious to hang he would do so soon enough.

On February 18, 1595, Southwell was removed by special commission of the Councilor from the Tower to Newgate Prison, a place which he knew well, for he had frequently slipped into it to visit recusants. He was aware that it was a waiting place for trial and the gallows, and that his quarters there would be in the dark, wet dungeon called Limbo.

Limbo was usually full of condemned robbers, but this winter evening Southwell had it quite to himself. He was surprised to find a bed, a fire and a candle. After the years in the Tower, he perhaps looked even younger and gentler than he had formerly, and somehow the under-keeper's heart was touched by his plight. Catholics had sent in food, and the keeper saw to it that the prisoner received his meals, which he said were better than any he had had since he went to the Tower. It was quite like him to express his gratitude for the kind things done for him.

After he had been there several nights, he was greeted one morning by a little old woman. She handed him a cup of hot broth, and said formally, "Good sir, God comfort you; you are to appear this morning before the judges. Drink this, that you may be stronger."

"My heart is full of joy," said Southwell, thanking the decrepit messenger, who had managed to convey to him the news that his trial was at hand.

His peace and happiness remained with him when he stood in Westminster Hall a few hours later. It was the scene of the trials of Thomas More and Bishop John Fisher, of Ralph Sherwin, Alexander Briant and Edmund Campion. Now it was his turn to be a witness to the Catholic Faith.

Bound with cords, he faced Sir John Popham, Chief Justice of the King's Bench and Sir Edward Coke, the Attorney General. Present also and irritating both lawyers with his rude, bold interruptions, was Her Majesty's Servant, Richard Topcliffe. A jury of twelve had been impaneled and told by the Chief Justice that Robert Southwell, the prisoner, was to be judged by the Statute of 1585, which made it treason for a subject of the Queen, born since her accession, to be ordained and return to England and there remain forty days.

Southwell, thin and pallid after his years in the Tower, waited under the great timbered ceiling while the Bill of Indictment was read. He was not distressed by its contents, for he well knew what they would be. The document asserted that Robert Southwell was a subject of the Queen, ordained since her accession, and that he had been present "like a false traitor" at Uxendon, June 26, 1592.

Anne Bellamy, now Mrs. Nicholas Jones, the only witness, was introduced to the court and sworn to deliver evidence.

When Southwell was called on to reply to the indictment, he said, "I confess I am a Catholic priest and I thank God for it, but I am not a traitor." Then he said that he did not deny that he was at Uxendon, for it was known to all that he had been drawn there like a mouse into a trap and there arrested, but that he was there not to commit treason but to administer the Sacraments.

The Chief Justice said, "Mr. Southwell, you must answer and either confess the indictment, or say 'not guilty.' "

"Not guilty of any treason," replied Southwell.

The Chief Justice said, "How will you be tried? By God and by your country?"

Quick as a flash came a loyal Englishman's answer: "By God and by you, for I would not lay upon my country the guilt of my condemnation."

Southwell was pained to think that, the law being so unjust, the jurors might seem guilty of his death, but finally he said, "If you will needs have it treason that I must lay upon the Jury, I will be tried by God and the country."

Then the jurors' names were called and they appeared, and Southwell was told that he might challenge them before they were sworn.

He answered, "I know no goodness in any of them, neither do I know any harm. According to charity, I judge the best and will challenge none."

The twelve jurors were sworn to try the young priest under the Statute of 1585.

The Attorney General, Sir Edward Coke, went down to the bar and explained to the jury the three points of the indictment and the fact that the prisoner could deny none of them; he stressed the fact that he had been born since the beginning of Queen Elizabeth's reign.

Sir John Popham interrupted and asked, "Mr. Southwell, how old are you?"

Southwell answered that he was close to the age of Our Saviour, Who lived on earth thirty-three years, for he himself was about thirty-four.

Topcliffe broke in indignantly, accusing him of likening himself to Christ. He began calling him "boy priest" and belittling him.

Topcliffe was silenced by the Court.

Southwell, having heard the Attorney General explain that his administering the Sacraments was treason under the Act of 1585, answered that he was familiar with that statute but it was entirely out of accord with God's law.

Argument ensued, and Southwell took occasion to remind the lawyers of the effect Topcliffe's torture had had on him, mind and body. And when Topcliffe interrupted and said that he had never been racked, Southwell turned to the Chief Justice and told that he had been tortured ten times so severely that the least of his tortures was worse than ten executions. He then described the hanging by the hands to the Chief Justice, who responded that all nations used torture. But Southwell, wishing to show up Topcliffe and to ease matters for future prisoners, said, ". . . . when information cannot be extracted from the victims by torture, I wish there might be some limit to it lest men be driven to desperation by the extremity of pain," a wish that showed him charitably mindful of souls.

Topcliffe said that he had proof that he had been ordered by the Council to torture the prisoner as he had, and tried to clear himself.

To everyone's amazement, the gentle priest looked directly at him and said in a clear voice, "You are a bad man." Southwell was determined that the Government know the extent of Topcliffe's private cruelty.

The Attorney General began to speak against Catholic practices and against the Pope, the Jesuits and Seminary priests.

Poor Anne Bellamy, who had been cruelly treated by Topcliffe and then married to his servant Nicholas Jones, was called as a witness. It was she who had betrayed Southwell almost three years before. Now she swore that he had taught her that the practice of verbal misleading was lawful.

Continually interrupted and reviled, Southwell attempted to explain, first to the Attorney General, and then to the Chief Justice, what must be presupposed to make a misleading answer lawful, but there was turmoil in the court. Sir Robert Cecil's intention had succeeded: feeling momentarily turned against the prisoner.

The men of the Jury were sent out to deliberate, and Sir John Popham suggested that Southwell might like to rest himself and have a drink. But Southwell asked to stay where he was, volunteering to be silent.

Presently, the twelve jurors filed back with their verdict, "Guilty."

Southwell said, "I pray God to forgive all who are in any way accessory to my death."

Sir John Popham then made a long speech warning Southwell that he must care for his soul. He then gave judgment "that he should be carried to Newgate from whence he came, and from hence to be drawn to Tyburn upon a hurdle, and there to be hanged and cut down alive, his entrails to be burned before his face, his head to be stricken off, his body to be quartered and disposed of at Her Majesty's pleasure."

Southwell listened, bowed, and thanked him.

There was a question as to whether he should return to Newgate by a boat on the Thames, but it was agreed that he would go quietly through the streets.

The writer of the old account known as *A Brefe Discourse*, from which the description of the trial comes, told how ". . . . he went joyfully with them through the streets, where many of his friends and acquaintance awayted his comynge only to see him, which they did to their great comforte."

Who those friends were cannot be ascertained. Possibly,

somewhere in the shadows, stood Richard Southwell, who had had the courage to petition the Queen for his son three years previously, and who, six years later, would die a Catholic in Fleet Prison. Perhaps the serving woman who has been called Melissa was there: she, too, would be rewarded, for years later on her death bed she spoke of Father Robert and asked for a priest. Maybe Frances Burrows managed to get a last glimpse of the holy priest whom she had protected from pursuivants; she was about to go to Louvain to become a nun, described in the convent annals as "inclined to be hasty." There seems little doubt that Mary and Edward Banister, Margaret and John Gage were among those who gazed at him "never knowinge him to looke better or more cherefully."

When Southwell was back in the Limbo at Newgate and had had a good meal sent in by the Catholics, he was visited by Protestant ministers commissioned to prepare him for death. Gentle as always, he was constrained to listen for three hours to men trying to turn him from the Faith for which he was about to die.

When the ministers had departed, another caller arrived, and there seems every reason to believe that this was a tall, dark young man with lively black eyes on whom the Queen was looking with favor: Charles Blount, the eighth Lord Mountjoy. The nobleman asked Southwell if he had been sent to detach the Queen's subjects from their obedience. To which Southwell replied that his only reason for returning to his country from Rome was to minister to souls, and, did he have it to do again, he would be willing to come from the farthest corner of the earth to procure the Queen's salvation.

Chapter 30

Southwell had meditated much on the Passion of Our Lord. Very often during the long night of February the twenty-first when he was in the Limbo dungeon of Newgate Prison, he must have thought of the Agony in the Garden, Christ's plea that the chalice might pass, and His acceptance: "Not My will, but Thine be done."

He begged God to give him strength to endure the hanging still ahead of him.

Years had passed since he and John Deckers had discussed martyrdom at Douay. He could lie now in the dark of the dungeon and think of Deckers, who would soon have an account of his sufferings. He could think, too, of good Father Philip Neri and his greeting *Salvete flores martyrum*, and of Campion, Sherwin, Shert, Briant, Kirby, Haydock and the others who had died for the Faith as Philip Neri had expected. How vivid now was the recollection of reading the account of Haydock's last hour! And Christopher Buxton and Christopher Bales had shown such courage as he hoped to have himself. He could only trust God to strengthen him, for he knew well the temptations that assail a man in the extremity of pain.

He lay so quiet, thinking and praying and commending his soul to God, that the keeper, wondering if he had died, went to the dungeon entrance and threw a light full on the prisoner's face. Southwell's expression was so radiant with hope and peace that the man never forgot it, and later he often spoke of his gentle prisoner.

On the morning of Friday, February the twenty-second, the keeper handed Southwell a cup of hot milk. He drank it thankfully, for he knew that he would need bodily strength to calm his mind during the day's ordeal. Then he gave the kindly keeper his cap as a token of farewell, and although the Catholics, wanting something that had belonged to their friend, begged the man for it, he could not be persuaded to part with it.

Southwell was now told that the horse-drawn hurdle was at the prison door. He went out, and lay down voluntarily on the rough, wheel-less vehicle. His wrists and arms were fastened to it with cords.

The journey to Tyburn started, the hurdle jouncing over the rough road.

An old countryman approached and called out, "God in Heaven bless and strengthen you."

Once when the hurdle slowed down, a young woman pushed close, knelt, and said, "Father Robert, pray for me that I may go forward in the way you have taught me."

His hands were tied, but he blessed her and said, "Dear Cousin, I thank you and I pray you to pray for me." Then he urged her to avoid the mud that began to spatter her as the horses started again and she continued alongside. In his anxiety for her safety, he spoke the words that identify her for us as his lovely cousin Margaret Copley Gage, "Do not risk your liberty; they will take you and put you in prison again." Obediently, she withdrew.

He kept his head as erect as possible, and when finally the hurdle neared Tyburn gallows, he raised himself somewhat and gazed on it joyfully.

Arrived, he was taken up from the hurdle and helped into a

cart that was set under the gallows. He stood a moment, in full view of the crowd, his expression serene and happy.

The Protestant Chaplain of the Tower began to preach to him, but he courteously asked him to desist, and sought the under-sheriff's permission to address those assembled. He tried to make the Sign of the Cross with his bound hands, and said clearly, " 'For whether we live, we live unto the Lord; or whether we die, we die unto the Lord. Therefore, whether we live or whether we die we are the Lord's.' " Having quoted that verse from St. Paul's Epistle to the Romans, he continued, "I am brought here to die, to perform the last act of this misery, and my time is very short for that. I most humbly desire of Almighty God that for the sake of Our Saviour Jesus . . . He pardon and forgive me all my sins and offenses that I have committed since my birth until now. . . . I acknowledge and confess that I am a priest of the Catholic and Roman Church (I thank God most highly for it) and of the Society of Jesus."

The Chaplain of the Tower broke in, but Southwell gently begged him not to interrupt, and continued, "I die a Catholic and hope to be saved by the Passion and Death of Our Saviour. Concerning the Queen's Majesty, God Almighty knows that I never meant or intended harm or evil against her; I have daily prayed for her, and yet in this short time which I have to live, I most humbly beseech and desire Almighty God . . . that He would vouchsafe that she may so use those gifts and those graces which God, Nature and fortune have bestowed upon her, that with them all she may both please and glorify God, advance the happiness of our Country, and purchase for herself the preservation and salvation of her body and soul.

"Next I commend into the hands of Almighty God this my poor Country, desiring Him, for His infinite mercy's sake, to reduce it to such perfect insight, knowledge and understanding of His truth, that thereby all may learn to please and glorify

180

God and gain health for their souls and eternal salvation. And lastly, I commend into the hands of Almighty God my poor soul, that it would please Him for His great mercy's sake to confirm and strengthen it with perseverance unto the end of this last conflict of mine; and this poor body of mine, as it shall please Her Majesty to dispose of. I humbly desire Almighty God that it please His goodness to take and accept my death, the last farewell to this miserable and unfortunate life, (although to me the manner of dying is most happy and fortunate) in full satisfaction for all my sins and offenses, and for the comfort of many others; which death, although it seem here disgraceful, yet I hope will prove in time to my eternal glory."

The hangman, who had previously opened Southwell's coat, now stripped off his shirt, put the halter about his neck and fastened it to the gallows. He was urged to ask the Queen's mercy, but he replied that if his coming to England had offended her, he begged her to forget it, and that he welcomed thankfully the punishment for his coming.

"God Almighty, help me," he prayed. "Blessed Virgin with all the Saints and Angels of Heaven, assist me."

Again he spoke to the bystanders, among whom was Lord Mountjoy: "I desire all Catholics to pray for me, that notwithstanding whatsoever may be said to trouble and disturb me in this conflict, I may yet this little while that I have to live, live a Catholic and die a Catholic."

Then, being accustomed to pray in Latin, he began, *"Sancta Maria, mater Dei, et omnes Sancti Dei, orate et intercedite per me!"* He made the Sign of the Cross and continued, "Into Thy hands, O Lord, I commend my spirit. . . . God be merciful to me, a sinner." Another Sign of the Cross, and again, *"In manus tuas, Domine, commendo spiritum meum."* A third time, he made the Sign of the Cross and said, "Into Thy hands . . ." Then he uttered verses from the psalm *Miserere*, the confident prayer of the penitent: "Restore unto me the joy of Thy salvation; and strengthen me with a perfect spirit."

The cart was drawn away from under his feet, and Southwell was left hanging from the gallows. Those looking on saw that his peaceful expression did not change, although because the halter was loose he remained alive.

The sheriff signed to the executioners to cut the rope so the victim would be conscious during the last moments of torture, for such was the custom. But the crowd, wishing to spare him the worst, cried out, "He prayed for the Queen."

Then Lord Mountjoy stepped out from the throng and forbade the executioners to cut the rope, since it was more merciful to let him hang right there until he died. A hangman, seeing his agony and his effort to make the Sign of the Cross, pulled him downward by the legs so that the end would come quickly.

Southwell closed his eyes and his expression became joyful. His life on earth had ended.

There was a hush over the crowd while the executioners treated the holy body as that of a traitor, and when the martyr's head was placed on a pike on London Bridge along with those before which it had been bared reverently many times, Catholics and Protestants, pursuivants and ministers, were saying with awe that this was a good man.

Select Bibliography

The Catholic Record Society Publications; the letters of the English martyrs edited by the late Fr. J. H. Pollen S.J. (Volume V, London, 1908); the translation of the *Liber Ruber* of the English College Rome (Volume 37, London, 1940); William Camden's *Britannia;* John Stowe's *Survey of London; The Harleian Society Publications; The Calendar of State Papers. Dom. Eliz. V. 1, 2, 3, 4;* Fr. T. F. Knox's *The First and Second Diaries of the English College, Douay* (London, 1878); Adam Hamilton's edition of *The Chronicles of the English Augustinian Canonesses of St. Monica's Louvain* (London, 1904); *The Letters of Sir Thomas Copley* edited by R. C. Christie and printed for the Roxburghe Club; many articles published in the "Month," including C. A. Newdigate's "A New Chapter in the Life of Blessed Robert Southwell," March, 1931; Father Philip Caraman S.J.'s recent editions of the autobiographies of Fr. William Weston S.J. and Fr. John Gerard S.J. *Vaux of Harrowden* by Fr. Godfrey Anstruther O.P. (1953); *Forgotten Shrines,* by Dom Bede Camm O.S.B.; *Secret Hiding Places,* Granville Squiers (Stanley Paul, London, 1933); Volume III of Father Philip Hughes' *The Reformation in England* (Macmillan Co. New York, 1954); Pierre Janelle's *Robert Southwell, the Writer* (Sheed & Ward, New York, 1935); Father James H. McDonald's *The Poems and Prose Writings of Robert Southwell S.J. A Bibliographical Study* (Oxford, Roxburghe Club, 1937); Professor Louis L. Martz's *The Poetry of Meditation* (Yale University Press, 1954); R. C. Bald's edition of Southwell's *An Humble Supplication to Her Majestie* (The University Press, Cambridge, 1953); Father J. M. de Buck S.J.'s edition of *The Spiritual Exercises and Devotions of Blessed Robert Southwell S.J.* (Sheed & Ward, London, 1931); *The Poetical Works of Robert Southwell* edited by Turnbull, and *The Complete Poems of Robert Southwell* edited by Grosart, and L. I. Guiney's *Recusant Poets* (Sheed & Ward).